Western School
1953-54

LIFE-READING SERVICE

ELSON-GRAY
BASIC READERS
BOOK FOUR

by

WILLIAM H. ELSON
and
WILLIAM S. GRAY

SCOTT, FORESMAN AND COMPANY
CHICAGO · ATLANTA · DALLAS · NEW YORK

ACKNOWLEDGMENTS

For permission to use copyrighted material, grateful acknowledgment is made to Robert M. McBride & Company for "Out-of-Doors" in *The Gentlest Giant* by Anna Bird Stewart; to Macrae Smith Company for "Bunnyboy Learns a Lesson" from "Bunnyboy's Disobedience" in *The Way of the Wild* by Clarence Hawkes; to Lew Sarett for "Six Little Sheep" from "Impasse"; to *The Youth's Companion* (now combined with *The American Boy*) for "A Bird House for Rent" from "House for Rent" by Russell Gordon Carter, for "The Tinker Plants a Tree" from "The Tinker's Willow," for "Jonathan Bartlett, a Pioneer Lad" from "Grandfather's Nickname" and for "Earning a Playground" from "The Field of Evil Weeds" by Edward W. Frentz, for "Sally's Sash" by Grace Kirkpatrick, for "Halloween" from "Warning" by Nancy Byrd Turner, for "Remembering Day" by Mary Wight Saunders, for "A Surprise Christmas" from "A Queer Christmas" by Marian Willard and for "A New Year's Leaf" from "A Word for New Year's" by Elizabeth Thornton Turner; to Nancy Byrd Turner for "For All Little Birds"; to Thornton W. Burgess for "Peter Rabbit Saves the Columbine"; to Clinton Scollard for "Whisperers" and for "We Must Wake and Work" from "Morning Song" in *A Boy's Book of Rhyme;* to Doubleday, Doran & Company for "The Wind" from *Taxis and Toadstools* by Rachel Lyman Field, copyright 1926, and for "Sheep-Shearing Day on Nantucket Island" from "Sheep-Shearing" in *Father's Gone A-Whaling* by Alice Cushing Gardiner and Nancy Cabot Osborne, copyright 1926; to John Stuart Coonley for "The Song of the Flag" from "Our Bonny Flag" by Lydia Avery Coonley Ward; to *Child Life* and the author for "How Andy Helped His Team to Win" from "The Race on Roller Skates" by Iris May Knight; to Noble & Noble for "Safety First in the City" from "Safety First for Children" by Benjamin Veit; to Bernard G. Richards Co., Inc., for "Every Child of Every Land" by S. Winsten from *Apples and Honey* by Nina Salaman; to D. Appleton & Company for "Alice Travels in Jungleland" from "On the March" in *Alice in Jungleland* by Mary Hastings Bradley; to the Missionary Education Movement of the United States and Canada for "Ting Fang Wins the Race for Sandals" from "Sandals" in *China Picture Stories* by Dorothy Rowe; to James B. Pinker and Son, Inc., Agents, for "Rumplestiltskin" from *Told Again* by Walter de la Mare; to A. Flanagan Company for "Benjamin Franklin Invents the Iron Stove" from "The Iron Stove" in *Boys and Girls of Colonial Days* by Carolyn S. Bailey; to The Century Company for "Oranges—America's Golden Harvest" from "California's Golden Harvest" by Burchard Bacon in *St. Nicholas*, and for "Rob's First Blackfish Drive" from "Rob Dunstan's First Blackfish Drive" by Edward Morgan in *Outdoor Stories Retold from St. Nicholas*.

"Lions and Dragons" from *Everything and Anything* by Dorothy Aldis, is reprinted through the courtesy of the author and the publishers, Minton Balch & Company, New York. "Climbing" from *A Dome of Many Coloured Glass* by Amy Lowell, is used by permission of and by arrangement with Houghton Mifflin Company. "Who Shall Be May Queen?" from *The Little Brown Bowl* by Phila Butler Bowman is reprinted with the consent of the publisher, Thomas Nelson & Sons.

Elson-Gray Basic Readers, Book Four, is a revision of *The Elson Basic Readers, Book Four*.

Copyright, 1931, 1936, by
SCOTT, FORESMAN AND COMPANY

Copyright, 1931, 1936, in the Philippine Islands by
Scott, Foresman and Company

Printed in the United States of America

PREFACE

The authors of the "Basic Readers" have attempted to provide an interesting, purposeful, and comprehensive reading course for the middle grades.

The primary aim of any reading course is to lead pupils to become voluntary and eager readers for both pleasure and information. To achieve this purpose the authors have assembled materials from the world-wide field of children's favorite readings. All of the selections included are of recognized worth in providing pleasure, imparting information, cultivating desirable attitudes, and developing appreciation. Such qualities are essential if the activities of the reading period are to result in enriched experience and permanent reading interests.

While selecting and classifying material for these readers the authors carefully surveyed the field of child literature in order to find selections that appeal strongly to children's interests. The stories and poems chosen have also been evaluated and graded in the light of present-day classroom realities. The material is so organized as to make each of the "Basic Readers" at its appropriate grade level the central core or framework of a larger reading plan. Each unit of *Basic Readers, Book Four* initiates a theme or field of interest which can be followed up and developed through the materials of various readers, library books, reference books, and other sources. Such a plan gives purpose and continuity to all reading materials available in the classroom. This correlation of varied reading-matter is made conveniently effective through the use of a special bibliography in the *Teacher's Guidebook* for *Basic Readers, Book Four*.

A systematic and carefully organized plan of teaching is provided in the "Guidebooks" for use in promoting growth of reading habits and interests from grade to grade. This plan is made concrete and usable through a series of carefully prepared lesson helps for each of the selections in *Basic Readers, Book Four*. This expert guidance helps teachers in making needed preparation for the day's lesson or for larger units of work. Additional exercises in the *Extension-Reading Work-Book* reinforce and extend the training of pupils in correct reading interests and habits. Thus basic reading attitudes and habits are developed through the purposeful use of interesting and significant content.

CONTENTS

                                                                     PAGE

YOUR BOOK COMRADE *(An Invitation to Boys and Girls)* 9

PART I
THE OUTDOOR WORLD

OUT-OF-DOORS	*Anna Bird Stewart*	11
NATURE CAN TELL US SECRETS	*(A Forward Look)*	12
BUNNYBOY LEARNS A LESSON	*Clarence Hawkes*	13
MISHOOK, THE BROWN BEAR CUB	*Ivan A. Slivitski*	22
SIX LITTLE SHEEP	*Lew Sarett*	32
A DAY WITH A PARTRIDGE FAMILY	*Ernest Thompson Seton*	33
PROTECTING THE BIRDS:		
A BIRD HOUSE FOR RENT	*Russell Gordon Carter*	42
FOR ALL LITTLE BIRDS	*Nancy Byrd Turner*	49
PETER RABBIT SAVES THE COLUMBINE	*Thornton W. Burgess*	50
LIONS AND DRAGONS	*Dorothy Aldis*	56
THE TINKER PLANTS A TREE	*Edward W. Frentz*	57
WHISPERERS	*Clinton Scollard*	63
THE WIND	*Rachel Lyman Field*	64
THE WONDERFUL WORLD	*William B. Rands*	65
A Backward Look		66

PART II
LITTLE AMERICAN CITIZENS

FLAGS	*Annette Wynne*	67
YOU CAN HELP YOUR COUNTRY	*(A Forward Look)*	68
ANNE RANDOLPH, A BRAVE AMERICAN GIRL	*Author Unknown*	69

CONTENTS

	PAGE
SALLY'S SASH ....Grace Kirkpatrick	74
THE SONG OF THE FLAG........Lydia Avery Coonley Ward.	79
JONATHAN BARTLETT, A PIONEER LAD ....Edward W. Frentz.........	80
HOW ANDY HELPED HIS TEAM...Iris May Knight	87
SAFETY FIRST IN THE CITY.......Benjamin Veit	98
A Backward Look	108

PART III
BOYS AND GIRLS OF OTHER LANDS

EVERY CHILD OF EVERY LAND....S. Winsten	109
EVERY LAND HAS ITS LITTLE CITIZENS ....(A Forward Look)	110
ALICE TRAVELS IN JUNGLELAND (Africa) ....Mary Hastings Bradley.....	111
MONI AND HIS GOATS (Switzerland) ....Johanna Spyri	124
TONINO TAKES HIS POTTERY TO THE FAIR (France)............H. Hill and V. Maxwell.....	135
TING FANG WINS THE SANDAL RACE (China) ....Dorothy Rowe	151
THE LITTLE TOY LAND OF THE DUTCH (Holland) ....Author Unknown	163
A Backward Look	164

PART IV
STORIES EVERYONE SHOULD KNOW

CLIMBING ....Amy Lowell	165
EVERYONE LIKES A GOOD STORY...(A Forward Look)	166
THE MIRACULOUS PITCHER.......Nathaniel Hawthorne	167
RUMPLESTILTSKIN ....Walter de la Mare.........	189
A DOG OF FLANDERS............Louise de la Ramée........	204
A Backward Look	214

CONTENTS

PART V
BUSY WORKERS AND THEIR WORK

		PAGE
WE MUST WAKE AND WORK	Clinton Scollard	215
HUNDREDS OF PEOPLE WORK FOR YOU	(A Forward Look)	216
BENJAMIN FRANKLIN'S IRON STOVE	Carolyn S. Bailey	217
ORANGES, AMERICA'S GOLDEN HARVEST	Burchard Bacon	226
SHEEP-SHEARING ON NANTUCKET ISLAND	A. Gardiner and N. Osborne	233
EARNING A PLAYGROUND	Edward W. Frentz	242
ROB'S FIRST BLACKFISH DRIVE	Edward Morgan	248
A Backward Look		256

PART VI
FAMOUS HEROES OF LONG AGO

LONG AGO AND FAR AWAY	Annette Wynne	257
EVERY LAND HAS ITS HEROES	(A Forward Look)	258
BEOWULF, THE BRAVE PRINCE	Clara E. Lynch	259
SIGURD, THE YOUNG WARRIOR	Clara E. Lynch	275
ROLAND, THE NOBLE KNIGHT	Clara E. Lynch	295
A Backward Look		318

PART VII
HOLIDAYS AND FESTIVALS

CHRISTMAS IN THE HEART	Author Unknown	319
HOLIDAYS ARE REMEMBERING DAYS	(A Forward Look)	320
HALLOWEEN	Nancy Byrd Turner	321
REMEMBERING DAY	Mary Wight Saunders	322
THE FIRST THANKSGIVING DAY	Bradford's History	323

CONTENTS

		PAGE
A Surprise Christmas	Marian Willard	338
The Christmas Fairy and Scrooge	Charles Dickens	346
A New Year's Leaf	Elizabeth Thornton Turner	363
Hearts Were Made to Give Away	Annette Wynne	363
Who Shall Be May Queen?	Phila Butler Bowman	364
A Backward Look		368
Good Books to Read		369
Glossary		375

YOUR BOOK COMRADE

An Invitation to Boys and Girls

I suppose some of you boys and girls think that I am only a book, only some sheets of paper with a lot of words printed all over me. But if you will make a friend of me, you will find that I am really the most enjoyable comrade you ever had.

Your schoolmates can play games with you, to be sure, and perhaps now and then can tell you something interesting that has happened to them. But every day I can tell you stories of exciting things that have happened all over the world—stories about all sorts of people and animals and heroes, at all sorts of times.

Let me take you by the hand and whisk you away to scenes in jungle Africa or lovely Switzerland or to the campfires of American pioneers. I shall speak to you with so many different voices that I cannot begin to introduce you to all of the interesting folk who will talk to you out of my pages. Just turn back for a moment to pages 5, 6, 7, and 8, called "Contents." You will see that I can tell you stories about seven different kinds of things.

First, I can lead you into the wonderland of Nature, where you will learn to know and love the animals, and birds, and flowers, and trees that live and grow all about you.

Then, if you will come with me, your Book Comrade, I can carry you into the homes of some brave and true American boys and girls. These will tell you how you, too, may become a helpful American citizen.

After visiting these American boys and girls, we shall go on a long journey across the sea to visit with boys and girls in other lands.

Then we shall go to other places, meet other people, and even travel to times of long ago and to the "land of make-believe." If you will look at Parts IV, V, VI, and VII in the "Contents," you will find the other interesting things we shall do.

Now, I have shown you some of the wonderful stories you may share with me if you will only make me your comrade. And one of the best things about me is the fact that I have thousands of brothers and sisters who will gladly be your comrades, too. If you look on pages 369, 370, 371, 372, 373, and 374, you will find the names of some of my brothers and sisters who can tell you just as interesting things as I can.

One more thing I must tell you. Perhaps, as I talk to you, I shall use some words you do not understand. But I will help you. On pages 375 to 383 you will find a "Glossary." It is a list of the harder words I have to use in talking to you. Here you may find what the words mean, and how to say, or pronounce, them. Don't forget to use this Glossary when you need it. I want you to understand everything I say.

PART · I

THE OUT DOOR WORLD

OUT-OF-DOORS

Sometimes, when in the house I stay,
Another house comes in my mind.
Its walls are hills far, far away;
The high-up roof with sky is lined;
The grass is carpet on the floors
Of this big house of out-of-doors.

For curtains there are leafy trees;
For lights there are the moon and sun;
One cannot ever lose the keys,
For it is home to everyone.
The front door's always open wide
To this big house of all-outside.

—*Anna Bird Stewart*

NATURE CAN TELL US SECRETS

THE world of the Out-of-Doors is full of secrets. There are so many of the secrets, and they are so interesting, that thousands of men and women and boys and girls are busy studying them. All around us are birds, animals, trees, and flowers. The facts about how they live and grow are as interesting as anything could be.

Do you know that Theodore Roosevelt, one of our great Presidents, spent hours and hours studying birds? A business man who lives near New York City became so interested in insects that he began to collect them. He now has over one thousand different kinds carefully kept in glass-covered boxes.

Come then with me, your Book Comrade, and I will help you find some of Nature's secrets. Let us go softly through the woods and fields. Here we shall find a half-grown Bunnyboy who has met with an adventure that has frightened him badly. We shall follow a mother bear and her four cubs as they hunt for food and get ready for their long winter's sleep. We shall watch a brave and wise mother partridge save her baby chicks from a hungry fox. I will show you many other interesting things, but the best thing that I can teach you is to keep your eyes and ears open when you go outdoors. Nature will tell you some of her secrets if you look and if you listen.

BUNNYBOY LEARNS A LESSON
Clarence Hawkes

Did you know that even a little rabbit has lessons to learn? One of these is to listen to his mother, for she knows many ways by which a rabbit may protect himself from his enemies. This story tells you how a little bunny got into trouble because he did not obey his mother.

MOTHER RABBIT'S PLAN

Bunnyboy was a half-grown "cotton-tail" rabbit, whose home was in the woods. He lived with his mother and brothers and sisters in the burrow— a nice warm hole that went down into the ground under an old tree stump.

One bright morning Mother Rabbit thought that she would go to a field where she knew there were some early cabbages.

"Children," she said, "if you are good while I am gone, I will bring you some juicy cabbage leaves. You must stay quietly at home."

But Bunnyboy followed his mother out of the burrow, saying, "I don't want to stay at home, Mother. Please take me with you."

"No, no, Bunnyboy!" said Mother Rabbit. "You are too young to go on such a long trip. But if you will keep very quiet, I will let you stay in a clump of bushes while I am gone. You can see all around you, and it will be almost as much fun as if you went with me."

So Mother Rabbit took Bunnyboy to a thick clump of bushes near the burrow and left him there alone. Then away she hopped to the cabbage field.

For a while Bunnyboy slept, dreaming of juicy cabbage leaves. But before long he awoke, sat up, and yawned. How he wished that his mother had taken him with her! Surely he was large enough to go. He was certain that he could run almost as fast as she could. He did not think his mother really knew how much he had grown or how well he could take care of himself.

WHAT HAPPENED WHEN BUNNYBOY RAN AWAY

For a long time Bunnyboy sat very still in the clump of bushes. But by and by he crept out carefully, and looked about.

As he sat there with the sunlight falling on his head and shoulders, he was the most beautiful little creature in the whole great woods. When he thought he heard a sound, his long ears wiggled this way and that, trying to find out what it was. His large, bright eyes looked carefully at everything near him. His nose tried to smell all the different scents of the woods.

Bunnyboy's mother had given him and his little brothers and sisters many lessons on the dangers of the woods. She had taught him to listen, to look, and to smell. For these were the three ways of protecting himself from his enemies—*listening, looking*, and *smelling*.

The woods were very quiet. Bunnyboy was sure that not one of his enemies was about. "There is no hawk or owl or fox in the whole woods," he said. "What fun it would be to jump around on the green forest carpet!" So he took a few hops away from the bushes.

Something said to him just as plainly as though his mother had spoken, "Go back, go back!" At first he listened to the voice and went back, but soon he was out in the green woods again, hopping from place to place.

He hopped upon an old log and ran back and forth on it; then he jumped into a clump of green ferns. Soon Bunnyboy was frisking and running through the woods, having the very best time he had ever had in his life.

But suddenly a strange scent came to him. It was not like anything that he had ever smelled before. At once he "froze" and waited. *Freezing* is one of the ways in which the wild creatures hide. It means to stay perfectly still. If a rabbit does not move, it is very hard to see him among the ferns and leaves. So Bunnyboy froze and waited.

Presently he saw a very strange animal coming slowly through the woods. He was a queer-looking fellow, covered with long, sharp quills. It was Mr. Porcupine, but as Mother Rabbit had never shown her children a porcupine, the young bunny did not know this stranger.

BUNNYBOY LEARNS A LESSON 17

Bunnyboy kept so still that Mr. Porcupine passed very close to him without seeing him. The young rabbit was terribly frightened. At last Mr. Porcupine was gone, and Bunnyboy was very glad. Then he thought he would go back to his clump of bushes. Off he started, but he could not find the bushes. Faster and faster he ran, but the more he ran, the farther away the bushes seemed.

At last he sat down to think. Where was the clump of bushes? His mother must have come home by this time. She would be very angry with him for running away.

Just at that moment he saw a large, white, round ball sticking to the inside of an old tree trunk. Never in his life had he seen such a ball as that; he would find out what it was.

So he crept up to the ball slowly, stopping to sniff the air and to listen. There was a strange buzzing noise coming from the ball that sounded like flies. Bunnyboy liked to catch flies, and here was a whole ball of them. What a fine time he would have! With a quick hop he went up and sniffed at the ball.

At the very first sniff he leaped into the air. For the ball was a hornets' nest, and hornets do not like to have rabbits hopping about their nest.

At once they flew out to punish him. They stung him on the nose and about the eyes. They stung his ears and shoulders and back. Bunnyboy ran wildly this way and that, with the hornets sticking to him. He jumped into the thickest ferns, rolling and tumbling, until at last he had rubbed them all off.

His nose, eyes, and ears burned as though they were on fire. Poor Bunnyboy rubbed them with his paw, but the more he rubbed, the more they burned. At last his eyelids began to swell and to close around his eyes.

BUNNYBOY LEARNS A LESSON

This frightened Bunnyboy terribly, and he started running again. If he could only find his mother before his eyes closed! But he could not find her, though he ran and ran.

Soon his eyelids were closed tightly, and he could not see to run. Then the poor little rabbit sat down in the woods, far, far from home.

Suddenly an awful thought came to him. Now that he could not see, any of his enemies could get him. The fox could creep up on him. The owl could swoop down upon him. Every sound he heard frightened him. At last he crawled into some bushes and lay there quietly, the most unhappy little bunny in the whole world.

HOW BUNNYBOY GOT HOME

Bunnyboy lay there a long time. At last he heard a noise; the sound was coming toward him. Was it an enemy or a friend? It sounded like a rabbit hopping along the path. But it might be a fox! Bunnyboy listened hard.

The sound came very close to him. He was almost sure that it was a rabbit hopping slowly along the path. So he made a queer little cry.

Then Bunnyboy's mother came hopping quickly along the path toward him. When she saw how terribly he had been punished for not obeying her, she did not scold him. He had learned his lesson. Very gently she led him down to the brook. Then she made him rub his face in the cool mud until it was covered. "Keep your eyes shut," she said. "Tomorrow we will come back to the brook and wash the mud off."

When Bunnyboy reached the burrow, he was so muddy that his brothers and sisters did not know him. But they made a soft place for him in the burrow and were very quiet all the rest of the day.

BUNNYBOY LEARNS A LESSON

Notes and Questions

1. What two things happened to Bunnyboy because he did not mind his mother?
2. Why did Bunnyboy's mother not punish him?
3. Name one thing that rabbits like to eat.
4. In what three ways can a rabbit find out that danger is near?
5. What are three enemies of the rabbit?
6. Why does a rabbit "freeze" when danger is near?
7. What word or words in List 2 mean the same as a word in List 1? Your first answer is *frisking—jumping about in play*.

List 1	List 2
frisking	to get bigger
scent	things growing close together
clump	took a quick smell
sniffed	to fly down swiftly
swell	a smell
swoop	jumping about in play

8. On what page of your Glossary can you find the meaning of "frisking"? Of "clump"? Of "swoop"?

Don't forget to use your Glossary when you need to find the meaning of a word, or when you want to know how to pronounce a word.

You will like to read some of these interesting rabbit stories and poems: "Raggylug," Parts I and IV, Seton (in *Wild Animals I Have Known*); "The Rabbit," Roberts, and "The Rabbit," King (in *Fifty New Poems for Children*); "Molly Cottontail, the Clever Freezer" and "The Rabbit Dance," Seton (in *Wild Animals at Home*).

MISHOOK, THE BROWN BEAR CUB

Ivan A. Slivitski

If someone asked you these questions about bears, could you answer them? In what kind of home do bears live? What do they eat? What do they do all winter? The story of Mishook will answer these questions, and tell you many other interesting things about bears.

IN THE DEN

It was March, and the air was cold; snow still covered the earth. But inside the cave in which lived Mishook, the brown bear cub, and his little sister, it was very warm.

The cubs had thick, dark-brown coats, narrow, blunt noses, and small, round ears. Their tails were so short that they could hardly be seen. Sharp claws peeped out from their toes.

Mishook's first home was the den that Mother Bruin had made for the winter which was just ending. In a well-hidden spot at the foot of a mountain, the old bear had dug a hole about twenty feet long, into which she dragged moss, dead leaves, and grass. When she had made these into a soft, warm bed, she piled up a heap of brushwood in front of the hole. In this warm den

Mishook and his sister were born. There they and their mother slept through the long, cold winter.

The bears' den was in a thick, black forest in Russia. No wonder this dark home pleased the Bruin family. Here they found everything that bears like: mountains and valleys, plenty of mushrooms and berries, and streams full of fish.

Mishook's mother always kept her children with her for two years. After that time they were strong enough to care for themselves and to live alone. Mishook and his little sister had an older brother and sister who were not yet quite old enough to leave their mother.

The winter had been long, and the cubs had grown very hungry. For four months they had been shut up in a den without eating, and now they were very thin. There had been nothing for them to do all day long but sleep.

Still, winter could not stay forever. It was now March, and spring had come at last. The air was warmer; the snow was gone; and the birds were singing gayly.

The mother now began to go for walks. Whenever she went out, she always left the little ones in the care of the older children. Then Mishook would tease his big brother, for he was full of fun. The older cub stood the teasing for a long time, but one day he gave Mishook such a slap on the head that the young bear cried aloud. That cry brought the mother into the cave. She flew at her older son, and boxed his ears. "You are no longer a young cub like Mishook," she said. "Do not be so rough with the little ones."

THE FIRST WALK

Mishook and his little sister grew bigger every day. At last they had grown so strong that their mother thought it was time to take them out for a walk. So one fine morning she told them to follow her. In front walked the old bear; behind her came Mishook and his young sister; last of all came the older cubs.

Mother Bruin showed her children how to find food. She squeezed some bugs in her paws and ate them. Then she caught a butterfly which was flying around her, and gave it to Mishook. How happy the cubs were as they frisked about!

The older cubs soon found some bushes covered with raspberries. Then the mother bear saw some young pine trees on the other side of a swamp, and went to feast upon the pale-green twigs.

But the older cubs forgot their young brother and sister, and wandered away. When the little ones found that they were alone, they started across the swamp to join their mother. At that moment the old bear looked up and saw them.

With an angry cry, she called to her older son, who was now far off. When he hurried to his mother's side, she gave him a blow on the head. The young cub knew very well why he was being punished. So he went quickly to Mishook and carried him back across the swamp.

Then he went to get his little sister and started back with her. But just before he reached the edge of the swamp, he let his sister fall into the water. At this his mother became so angry that she gave him another hard blow. Then she herself carried the young cub to the shore.

They now went on their way. But after a time Mother Bruin lay down to rest, while the older cubs walked off, looking for something to eat.

"Well, my dears," the old bear asked the little cubs, "is it not nice to go for a walk?"

"Oh, mother dear, it is so nice, so very nice that we never want to go back to the den any more," answered Mishook and his sister.

Just then Mishook saw something that surprised him. "Oh, mother!" he cried, "what are those two ugly creatures up there in that tree?"

"What ugly creatures do you mean?" scolded his mother. "Don't you know your own brother and sister? Look how high they have climbed!"

"Mother, do let us climb up to them!" cried the younger cubs eagerly.

"Climb if you like," said the old bear.

The cubs ran toward the tree. From the very first, they found it easy to climb, for their sharp claws helped them to hold on to the bark. But getting down again was not so easy.

After this the happy bears went on with their pleasant walk. All at once a breeze came up,

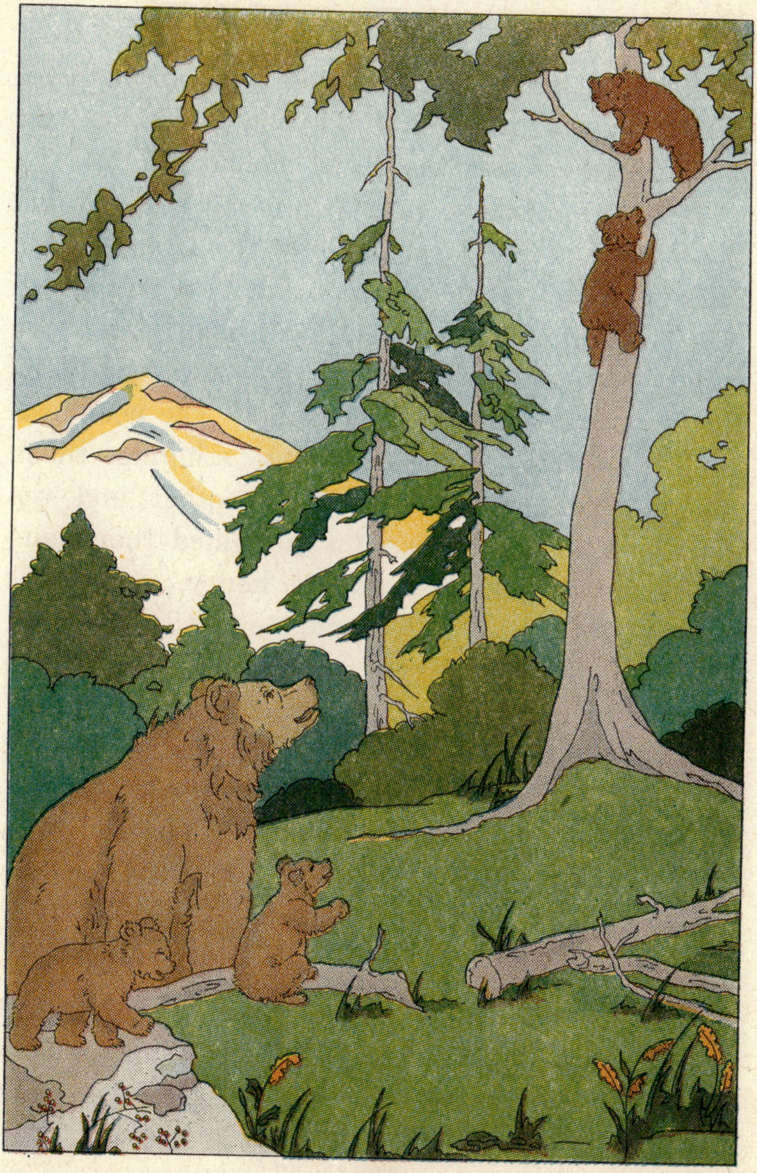

bringing the smell of something sweet to Mishook. What could it be? He did not know; but his mother did—it was the smell of honey.

Then the whole Bruin family set off to find the honey. They trotted along for about half a mile before they reached an old hollow tree which was the home of the bees. Mother Bear broke the tree open with her strong paws, and the bear family began to eat the honey. The poor bees tried to drive them away by stinging them. But this did not trouble the mother and the older cubs. Their thick fur protected them, and they went on eating the sweet honey.

Mishook enjoyed the honey, too, until one angry bee stung his tender nose. Then the little cub growled furiously, shook his head, jumped, snorted, and spun around like a top. At last he beat off the bee with his paws.

By this time the sun was high in the sky. The Bruin family grew very warm in their heavy fur; so they hurried back to the cool, shady den.

GETTING READY FOR WINTER

As the summer passed, the cubs grew bigger and stronger every day. They did nothing but eat, and yet the fishes, bugs, nuts, and berries were not enough for them.

Mother Bruin saw that her children were always hungry. "How thin you are!" she cried. "You cannot sleep through a whole winter with no more fat than you have now, my children. You must eat meat. Then you will grow fat enough to sleep all winter without eating."

So she went toward the village until she came to a large pasture. There she killed a fine black horse, which she dragged into the forest. She and her cubs feasted on the fresh meat until they had all they wanted. Then they crept far into the dark woods and lay down for a quiet sleep.

From this time on, each day brought new trouble to the village. Bee-hives were robbed; one farmer lost a cow, another a horse. The Bruin family became very, very fat. As for Mishook, he was as round as a log.

At last autumn came, and the mother bear made a large, new den. In October the whole family slept in it most of the time. Once in a while the mother went out to hunt for food. Then she would say to her children, "Don't go far away, my dears; the snow may fall at any moment, and we must not leave tracks in the snow. Men will find us and kill us if we do."

Soon the north wind began to blow, rain fell

often, and the mornings became colder. The birds had long ago flown away to a warmer country. By this time the bears had grown very sleepy. Now Mother Bruin would not let her cubs eat much, but she told them to drink all the water they wanted.

One day, when they were all in the cave, she said: "It is time to take a long rest, children. We are not going out again until springtime. Mishook and his little sister must lie down in the back of the den, and the older cubs in front of them. I will stretch myself near the opening."

Mother Bruin then closed the mouth of the

MISHOOK, THE BROWN BEAR CUB

cave with brushwood, and the bears fell asleep. The den was soon covered deep with snow. Not again until spring would Mishook and his family leave the warm cave.

Notes and Questions

1. To show that bears eat many different kinds of food, make a list of five things these bears ate.

2. Below are three answers to the question, "Why can bears go without food all winter?" Which is the best answer?

   (a) They get so fat before winter begins.
   (b) They have a warm den.
   (c) They do nothing but sleep.

3. Why did the mother bear make the youngest cubs walk in the middle?

4. Why did she have the youngest cubs sleep far back in the cave?

5. Bunnyboy had many enemies. What was the bears' greatest enemy?

6. Why did Mother Bruin not want to leave tracks in the snow?

7. Why do bears like to live where it is cool?

8. What tells you that bears have good noses?

9. Did you find some hard words—such as *blunt, brushwood, twigs,* and *pasture?* Don't forget to use the Glossary when you need to.

You will enjoy reading "Bruin's Boxing Match," Roberts (in *Child-Library Readers, Book Four*); "Johnny Bear and Other Winter Sleepers," Hawkes (in *Child-Library Readers, Book Three*).

SIX LITTLE SHEEP

Lew Sarett

Six little sheep,
   Bleating in the sun,
Don't know which
   Way they should run.

Fence to the left;
   Fence to the right;
Before them a mouse
   That fills them with fright.

Nothing to do
   But wheel and go—
A little too much
   For sheep to know.

A DAY WITH A PARTRIDGE FAMILY

Ernest Thompson Seton

Perhaps you have thought that the wild creatures of the woods and fields do nothing all day but eat and frisk carelessly about. But their lives are quite different from that. When they are still very young, they begin to learn how to find food and how to hide from their enemies. This story tells how some baby partridges, toddling after their mother, met with a dangerous adventure.

HOW MOTHER PARTRIDGE FOOLED THE FOX

Down the side of Taylor's Hill Mother Partridge led her baby chicks toward the meadow and the sparkling brook. The little partridges were only one day old, but they were already quick on foot, and their mother was taking them for the first time to drink.

Mother Partridge walked slowly, for the woods were full of enemies. From her throat came a soft cluck. It was a call to the little balls of down who came toddling after her on their tiny pink legs. They peeped softly if they were left even a few inches behind. There were twelve of

---

From "Redruff," in *Wild Animals I Have Known;* published by Charles Scribner's Sons. By permission of the publishers.

them, but Mother Partridge watched them all. She also watched every bush and tree, and the whole woods, and the sky itself.

Always this mother was looking for enemies, and an enemy she found when she reached the edge of the wooded slope. Across the meadow she could see a fox. He was coming toward her and her brood, and in a few moments would be close enough to catch their scent in the wind. The mother partridge knew that there was not a minute to lose.

"*Krrr! Krrr!*" (Hide! Hide!) cried the mother in a low voice; and the tiny partridges, hardly bigger than acorns and only one day old, scattered a few inches apart to hide. One hid under a leaf, another ran between two roots, a third crawled into a hole, and so on, until all were hidden but one. This one could find no hiding-place; so he squatted on a broad, yellowish brown chip of wood and lay very flat and still. Then he closed his eyes tight, feeling sure that now he was safe from being seen. And he was nearly right; for he looked almost like the chip itself. One by one the little partridges stopped their frightened peeping, and all was still.

Mother Partridge did not wait for the fox to

A DAY WITH A PARTRIDGE FAMILY

reach the spot where her twelve little ones were hiding. This wise mother flew straight toward the beast and dropped a few yards to one side of him. Then she flung herself on the ground, flopping as though lame—oh, so lame—and whining like a puppy. By pretending that she was lame, she was going to lead Mr. Fox away from her babies, and then fly away from him herself.

Delighted to see a partridge beside him, the fox sprang at the bird. But when he was almost sure he had caught her, she flopped just a foot or so out of his reach.

He followed with another jump and would have caught her this time surely, but somehow a little tree came between them, and the partridge dragged herself away and hid behind a log. He snapped his jaws and bounded over the log, while she made another forward jump and tumbled down a bank. The eager fox almost caught her tail, but, strange as it seemed, the faster he ran and leaped, the faster she seemed to go.

To the fox it was more than surprising! He could hardly believe that in five minutes he, the swift-footed fox, had not caught a bird whose wing appeared to be injured.

Mother Partridge seemed to get stronger as the fox followed swiftly. After a quarter of a mile of racing—that was all *away* from Taylor's Hill—the bird suddenly rose with a whirr and flew off to some thick bushes that lay at quite a distance from the hill. Then the fox knew that he had been made a fool of, and walked away.

Mother Partridge flew back to the little fuzz-balls she had left hidden in the woods. She went to the very grass-blade she had last stepped on. There she stood for a moment, pleased at the perfect stillness of her children. Even at her step not one of them stirred. The little fellow on the chip

37

only closed his eyes a tiny little bit harder, till the mother said:

"*K-reet!*" (Come, children!) At once every hiding-place gave up its little baby partridge. The wee fellow on the chip opened his eyes and, with a sweet little "*peep, peep,*" ran to his mother. Then all the other tiny balls of down joined in the peeping, and were very happy.

WHAT MOTHER PARTRIDGE TAUGHT HER BABIES

The sun was hot now, and there was an open place to cross on the way to the water. So the mother spread out her tail like a fan, and gathered the little things in the shadow under it. In this way she kept off all danger of sunstroke until they reached the bushes by the stream.

Here a cotton-tail rabbit leaped out and gave them a great scare. But he was an old friend; and one of the many things the little partridges learned that day was that Bunny always wants to live in peace with his neighbors.

And then came the drink—the purest of running water. At first the little fellows didn't know how to drink, but they watched their mother, and soon learned to drink as she did. There they stood in a row along the edge of the brook, twelve little

A DAY WITH A PARTRIDGE FAMILY

brown-and-golden balls on twenty-four little pink-toed feet, with twelve sweet little golden heads bowing and drinking.

Then Mother Partridge led her brood to the meadow. Here there was a great grassy hump, which she had seen some time before. This was an ants' nest. The mother stepped on top of it, and then gave half a dozen rakes with her claws. The ant-hill was broken open and its insides scattered.

At once the ants swarmed out. Some ran around the hill, while a few of them began to carry away fat, white eggs. The old partridge, coming to her children, picked up one of these juicy-looking eggs and clucked. Then she dropped it, picked it up again, and clucked, and finally swallowed it.

The young ones stood around, watching. Then one little fellow—the one that had sat on the chip—picked up an ant-egg, dropped it a few times, and then swallowed it; so he had learned to eat. Within twenty minutes even the smallest partridge had learned. And a merry time they all had scrambling after the eggs which their mother sent rolling down the sides of the ant-hill. Soon every young partridge had swallowed so many eggs that he could eat no more.

Then the mother led her children up the stream. On a sandy bank, well hidden by bushes, they lay all that afternoon. They learned how pleasant it was to feel the cool dust running between their hot little toes. They lay on their sides as their mother did and scratched happily with their tiny feet.

That night Mother Partridge took her little ones to a dry thicket near by. There, among the dead leaves and under the bushes, she covered them with her soft feathers. The wee cuddling things peeped in their sleep and snuggled against her warm body.

A DAY WITH A PARTRIDGE FAMILY

Notes and Questions

1. How did Mother Partridge fool the fox? Be ready to read the lines that tell how she did it, or to tell it in your own words.

2. How did Mother Partridge protect her chicks from the hot sun? Find the lines that tell.

3. Name two things the mother taught the baby chicks on their first day. Perhaps you can find more than two things they learned.

4. On page 33 Mr. Seton, the author of the story, calls the chicks "little balls of down." Find two other word pictures of the chicks.

5. Here are five words, and five sentences, each with a word left out. Choose the right word for each sentence. Your first answer is (a) *sparkle*.

sparkle   downy   hump   appeared   thicket

(a) The snow and ice .... in the sunshine.
(b) In the nest were four .... little robins.
(c) He stumbled over a .... of dirt.
(d) The rabbit hid in the ....
(e) The little brown bear .... to be hurt.

6. Be ready to read the lines that tell about the picture on page 35.

7. Find a sentence on page 36 that tells just what is happening in the picture on page 37.

8. How do you pronounce *tiny*? Look in the Glossary to see if you are right.

You would like to read "Bob White! Wheat's Ripe!" Whitsett, and "The Old Possum and Her Kittens," Reid (both in *Child-Library Readers, Book Four*); and "The Dusky Ducks," Patch (in *Holiday Pond*).

A BIRD HOUSE FOR RENT
Russell Gordon Carter

Suppose that you love grass and flowers and trees very much, and that you have always lived where you could enjoy them in your own yard. Then suppose you had to move to a place where there were none of these pleasures. What would you do? You may be greatly surprised to read what the girl and boy in this story did.

When the Gilberts first moved to the city, they took rooms in a boarding-house, and began to look for a new home.

"I hope it will have a big back yard with grass and flowers," said Elise.

"Yes," said her brother Frank, "and I hope it will have a tree where the birds can play."

But it was not easy to find a house that pleased them. For six weeks the Gilberts hunted and hunted. Then at last one afternoon, when Frank and Elise came home from school, their mother said, "Well, we have found a house."

"Has it a back yard with flowers?" asked Elise.

"And a tree?" said Frank.

"Well, not exactly," replied Mrs. Gilbert, slowly.

On the first of the next month the Gilberts

moved into the new home. At once Frank and Elise hurried out to the back yard. What they found was just smooth concrete. There was not a blade of grass anywhere, or even a small bush. In one corner stood a tall white flagpole.

"Well," said Frank. "Concrete instead of grass, and a pole instead of a tree!"

"I don't see what we can do about it," answered Elise. "Nothing will grow here, and I don't suppose that we shall be able to make friends with the birds. But we can't help it."

The next day Frank went out into the yard and looked at the flagpole for a long time. Then without a word, he went down into the cellar.

All the rest of the afternoon Elise heard the sound of Frank's hammer and the rip, rip of his saw. She guessed that he was making something to earn a little money; perhaps it was a dog house for his uncle's new puppy.

Several days later Elise happened to be out in the yard. As she stood looking at the hard concrete, she thought to herself, "It seems pretty lonesome." Then something made her look up at the flagpole. Two little wrens were fluttering around the ball at the top!

"Well," cried the surprised girl. "I do believe birds would come here to live if they had only half a chance!"

She walked over to the corner of the yard and stood looking down at the foot of the pole. There she saw a low place in the concrete that looked like a huge saucer. All at once a happy thought came to her and she began to smile. "I know what I'll do," she said. "And won't Frank be surprised!"

That evening she borrowed Frank's blue pencil, and went to her room. When her father came home, she met him at the door; and Frank heard them talking in low voices.

After supper Elise and her mother went for a

walk. As soon as they were out of sight, Frank went down to the cellar. When he came back, he was carrying a little wooden house, which he showed to his father proudly.

"Tomorrow will be Elise's birthday, you know," he said. "I must get up in time to surprise her." Frank wondered why his father smiled as though he knew something funny.

"I'll tell you what I'll do," said Mr. Gilbert. "If you leave the bird house with me, I'll put it up on the pole late this evening. Then the surprise will be all ready for her the first thing tomorrow morning."

Frank went down the street to see a boy, and did not come back until it was too dark to take a look at the bird house. Elise heard him come in, and she smiled to herself as she thought how surprised he would be in the morning.

While Frank was dressing the next morning, he heard Elise calling him from the foot of the stairs. "Frank," she cried, "I have something to show you."

Frank came running down the stairs. As he walked with his sister toward the back door, he could hardly keep from laughing at the thought of his birthday secret.

"Look," said Elise. "We haven't a tree in our back yard, but we have—" Suddenly she stopped. "Well, I declare!"

Frank was as much surprised as she. They both stood looking at the flagpole, which had changed a good deal since they last saw it. High up on the pole was a neat little bird house; on it was the sign, "House for Rent."

A little below it was another sign, "Bath Downstairs," with a hand pointing to the foot of the pole. The little hollow place there was filled to the edge with clear, sparkling water.

"Why, Frank," cried Elise, "I didn't dream it was a bird house that you were building!"

"And I never thought of a bird bath," laughed Frank, "even if you did borrow my pencil to make the sign!"

Just then two little wrens flew to the fence and fluttered down for a splash in the pool. While the children were watching the strange sight, their mother and father came out.

"Well!" said Father, "I think that between the two of you, you've made a very nice home for the birds. Wait a minute—"

He went into the house and soon came back with a large box full of nasturtium and pansy plants.

A BIRD HOUSE FOR RENT

"Your mother and I want to share in the surprise, too," he said, as he set the box of beautiful flowers down near the little pool.

"Oh, thank you, Father and Mother!" said Elise, "you have all given me a happy birthday."

Then they all went away from the flagpole to see what would happen. Pretty soon the two wrens fluttered up to the tiny bird house and went inside. It was easy to see that they wanted to rent the new home.

"Who says we can't have birds, even if we haven't any grass or green trees!" cried Elise.

"Now our yard has a bird bath and flowers and everything!" cried Frank.

"And all on a concrete lawn, too," laughed Mrs. Gilbert.

"Since our bird house is rented, we may as well take the sign down," said Father. "Houses don't stay empty long these days."

Notes and Questions

1. Which sentence—(a), (b), or (c)—best tells what this story is about?
    (a) How a boy surprised his sister on her birthday.
    (b) How a family made their back yard look better.
    (c) How a brother and sister got some birds to come and live in their back yard.
2. Which sentence below best tells what we learn from this story?
    (a) We should try to make our yards beautiful.
    (b) We should be thoughtful of each other's birthdays.
    (c) Birds will come and live with us if we give them homes.
3. If you have bird houses or baths in your yard, tell what birds use them.
4. Do birds help us in any way? Perhaps you know, or can find out.

You will like to read "A Vireo at Home," Baynes; "The Bird That Makes Clay Pots," Seton; "Red Riding Hood," Whittier (in *Child-Library Readers, Book Four*); "To Let," Stewart (in *The Birds Began to Sing*); and "Twenty Foolish Fairies," Turner (in *Magpie Lane*).

FOR ALL LITTLE BIRDS

Nancy Byrd Turner

God who lovest all things,
Folks and flocks and herds,
Lend an ear to this my prayer
For the little birds.

Bless them flying, feeding, resting;
Bless them singing, playing, nesting;
Keep them well in every weather,
Safe and warm in shine or storm,
Glad and gay, day by day,
All the birds together!

PETER RABBIT SAVES THE COLUMBINE
Thornton W. Burgess

The very last sentence in this story says "Why, oh, why, do people want to destroy such beautiful things?" What do you suppose the beautiful things are?

PETER AND HUMMER VISIT THE COLUMBINE

Peter Rabbit had spent a happy night frisking about in the Old Pasture. Just as he was ready to start for his home in the Briar Patch, early in the morning, he heard a humming sound.

Peter looked up, frightened. He was afraid it was his enemy, Redtail the Hawk. But no, it was only his friend, Hummer the Humming-bird, who now swooped down so close to Peter's head that the rabbit ducked.

"What are you trying to do?" he cried angrily.

"Just trying to show my happiness," answered Hummer. "Isn't spring a beautiful time of year? I always love to visit the Old Pasture when the columbine is in bloom."

Peter pricked up his long ears. "Columbine? Columbine?" he said. "I suppose that is a flower. You never seem to be much interested in anything but flowers."

PETER RABBIT SAVES THE COLUMBINE 51

Z-z-zoom—z-z-zoom—came Hummer close to one of Peter's long ears. "Of course the columbine is a flower!" he cried. "It is one of the most beautiful of all spring flowers. Only a few moments ago I found the first one I have seen this year."

"Of course I know the columbine!" Peter cried. "It is so long since I saw it last spring that for a few minutes I could not remember it. But I remember it now, and I know just where it is."

With a quick hop Peter started up one of the paths that led to the other end of the Old Pasture. Lipperty-lipperty-lip he ran, while Hummer darted on ahead. In a few minutes Peter came to a long, low pile of rocks. He hopped up on one of the rocks, and looked all about.

There, close beside him, were several nodding

blossoms. On the outside, these lovely flowers were scarlet, but inside they were yellow. Their slender stems had beautiful light-green leaves.

Hummer darted from flower to flower, sticking his long bill into each, and Peter knew that these blossoms were as sweet as they were beautiful.

A little briar bush was growing right near where Peter had found the columbine. Here he could sit and be safe, and at the same time look at the nodding blossoms. From time to time he dozed off. Between little naps he watched the lovely columbine blossoms.

HOW PETER FOOLED THE CHILDREN

It was about the middle of the morning when Peter heard the merry laughter and shouting of children. From the sound he knew that the children were at the other end of the Old Pasture. When their voices told him that they were coming close to where he was sitting, he thought he would find out who they were and what they were doing.

Peeping out from beneath the briars, Peter saw two boys and a girl. In their hands were flowers, and Peter saw that the children were looking for more flowers. He heard the little girl give a cry

PETER RABBIT SAVES THE COLUMBINE

of delight when she found a patch of beautiful arbutus. From where Peter sat, he saw her pull it up, roots and all, and then break off some of the roots.

Peter was very angry. He knew that the little girl was just thoughtless, but soon there would be no arbutus left, if everyone were thoughtless. Later he saw one of the boys do just what the little girl had done.

Then he noticed that some of the flowers in their hands were badly wilted. Peter knew how lovely the growing flowers had been, and he could not understand why the children should want these sickly, wilted blossoms. But they seemed to want them and to want more, too, for they were hunting everywhere.

Then, Peter suddenly remembered the columbine blossoms. The children would be sure to find them, and take not only the blossoms, but the whole plants. He must do something about it, and do it quickly. But what could he do?

All of a sudden Peter remembered how often he had been chased by boys. "I'll have to use my long legs to save the columbine," he said.

Quickly he jumped out into one of the winding paths, and up this path he hopped. Just ahead of him he saw one of the boys. Peter stopped. Then he thumped the ground with his long hind feet. The boy heard the thump and turned. Of course he saw Peter at once. Right then and there he forgot all about the flowers. "A rabbit!" he shouted. "Here's a rabbit!"

Then the other little boy and the little girl came running. Peter hopped into the bushes at one side and, a little later, ran out of them. Away he went down the path, and hopped into a briar bush. After him raced the children. They saw him in the bush and tried to drive him out. When he saw a good chance, away he went again, lippertylip, for another briar bush.

The excited children followed, but Peter wasn't at all afraid. It was just a game to him, a game he had often played before. And so, little by little, the rabbit led the children far away from where the columbine was growing. Then, when they were quite tired out, Peter hopped back to the little briar bush to watch the columbine blossoms. "Of course you don't know it," he said to them, "but I saved you with my long heels. Why, oh, why, do people want to destroy such beautiful things?"

NOTES AND QUESTIONS

1. Which of these three things is Mr. Burgess trying to tell in this story?
    (a) That rabbits and birds love flowers.
    (b) That rabbits are clever animals.
    (c) That we must not pick wild flowers.
2. Find and be ready to read the lines that prove your answer to Question 1.
3. Be ready to read the lines that tell how the columbine looks.
4. How did Peter fool the children? Can you think of something in the partridge story that reminds you of his trick?

There is a book of stories by Mr. Burgess called *The Burgess Flower Book for Children*. You would enjoy reading it.

LIONS AND DRAGONS

Dorothy Aldis

Snap-Dragons and Dande-Lions
Are not so very wild—
I never yet saw one forget
And try to hurt a child.

A Dande-Lion never roars
Not even once, for fun;
Nor waves his tail with angry wail—
Because he hasn't one!

A Snap-Dragon will never snap
No matter how he feels,
Except to try to catch a fly
To brighten up his meals.

THE TINKER PLANTS A TREE
Edward W. Frentz

Trees are the oldest living things in the world! Today there are growing in our country trees that were here when Columbus came to our land. Some of them were here even hundreds of years before he came.

"Only God makes trees, but sometimes we can help Him," said the Tinker in his story.

One day, when my Grandfather Gifford was about seven years old, he looked across the road to his father's blacksmith shop. He saw someone sitting on the bench by the door and went over to find out who it was.

There he saw a little old man, with thick, bushy eyebrows and bright blue eyes. At the old man's side was an open bag, in which grandfather could see some tools and sheets of tin. The man was a traveling tinker, who came once or twice a year to mend leaky pans and pails.

The old man was eating his lunch, a slice or two of bread, a bit of cold meat, and a cold potato. It seemed so poor a lunch, that grandfather went to the house and brought two big apples from the cellar. The old man thanked him and ate the apples. Then he got up, and went down to the brook for a drink of water. In a few minutes he came back and sat down on the bench near the door.

"Now, my boy," he said, "we will make a tree grow down by the brook. There should be one, for shade."

"Make a tree!" cried grandfather. "How can we make a tree? I thought only God made trees."

"True," said the old man. "Only God makes trees, but sometimes we can help Him."

With these words, he took from the bench at his side a stick that he had cut somewhere and had been using for a cane. It was slender and straight, and its smooth bark was a beautiful light-green color.

"From this," said the tinker, "we will make a tree in which the birds shall build their nests. Under it the animals shall find shelter from the hot sun. But first let us make some music. Take this stick down to the brook, and dip it in the water."

My grandfather took the stick and did as the old man had told him. When he came back, the tinker had a large knife open in his hand. With it he made a cut through the bark of the stick, about a foot from one end. By holding the

THE TINKER PLANTS A TREE

knife still, and turning the stick slowly toward him in his fingers, he cut the bark all the way round. Then he cut a big notch, near the end of the stick and, farther down, he made four or five smaller notches. Last of all, he laid the stick across his knee, and, turning it slowly, began to tap it gently with the handle of the knife.

After a while the tinker laid down the knife, took the stick in both hands, and gave it a little twist. At once, grandfather heard something pop. Then he saw the bark slip from the stick above the knife-cut, all in one long, round piece.

After this the old man cut away more than half of the part of the stick from which he had slipped the bark. Across the upper end he made a smooth, slanting cut. Then he told grandfather to wet the stick again, after which he slipped the bark back to its place.

The old tinker put the end of the stick in his mouth, placed his fingers over the smaller notches, and began to blow. As he lifted first one finger and then another, out of the deep notch came sweet music like the voice of a bird singing a long way off.

While the old man played, he seemed to forget all about grandfather. By and by he laid down the whistle, smiled, and said, "Come. Bring the whistle. Now we shall make the tree."

They walked down to the brook together, and crossed over on some stepping-stones to a place where the ground was soft and black and wet. While the boy held the stick, the old man pushed it far down into the mud until it stood up straight, with the whistle at the upper end.

Then the old man bowed to the stick, and said:

"Little brother, we leave you here, where you will never be hungry or thirsty. You have made your sweet music for us today. But when you have grown tall and strong, gentle winds will make even sweeter music among your branches."

THE TINKER PLANTS A TREE

A little while after that the old man put on his pack and went away; but my grandfather could not forget him or what he had done. Almost every day the little boy looked at the stick by the brook. The whistle at the top began to dry up, and the loose bark cracked open and fell off, until it seemed as if the whole stick must be dead.

But one day my grandfather saw a tiny bud below the place where the whistle had been. The bud became a little sprout, and the sprout became a little branch. Then other branches followed, until the stick was indeed a little tree.

Year after year it grew taller and stronger.

until "The Tinker's Willow" was known as the greatest tree in all the countryside. The birds did, indeed, build their nests among its branches, the winds made sweet music among its leaves, and the cattle lay in its shade on hot summer days.

NOTES AND QUESTIONS

1. Why did the Tinker plant the tree? Find lines that tell, and be ready to read them.

2. On page 60, what did the Tinker call the tree?

3. Be ready to tell in your own words just how the Tinker made the whistle.

4. Find the lines that tell what the picture on page 61 shows. Be ready to read them.

5. Make a list of ways in which trees are useful to us. Read "The Boy Who Hated Trees" (in *Child-Library Readers, Book Three*) to find out how Dick learned to love trees. You will also enjoy "The Old Pear Tree," Fabre (in *Child-Library Readers, Book Four*); and "What the Tree Promised," Frentz (in *American Childhood*, April, 1930).

WHISPERERS

Clinton Scollard

Whenever I go up or down
Along the roadway into town,
I hear a busy whispering there
Among the trees high up in air.

It's clear to one who's not a fool
That trees have never been at school;
And if you ask me why I know—
It is because they whisper so!

THE WIND

Rachel Lyman Field

Be very polite to the Wind, my child,
For the Wind's a fellow both wise and wild.
A tramp, he travels from town to town
With his bag of tricks, like a circus clown.

He never rests; he never tires;
He blows on grass blades and gilded spires,
On tasseled corn and fields of wheat,
And the skirts of the farmer's wife so neat.

If you chance to meet him, always say,
"Wind, are you feeling well today?"
And be sure you lift the cap from your head,
Or the Wind may do it himself, instead!

THE WONDERFUL WORLD
William B. Rands

Great, wide, beautiful, wonderful World,
With the wonderful water round you curled,
And the wonderful grass upon your breast—
World, you are beautifully dressed!

The wonderful air is over me,
And the wonderful wind is shaking the tree;
It walks on the water, and whirls the mills,
And it talks to itself on the tops of the hills.

You friendly Earth, how far do you go,
With the wheat-fields that nod and the rivers that flow,
With cities, and gardens, and cliffs, and isles,
And people upon you for thousands of miles?

Ah! you are so great, and I am so small,
I hardly can think of you, World, at all;
And yet, when I said my prayers today,
A whisper within me seemed to say:
"You are more than the Earth, though you're such a dot;
You can love and think, and the Earth cannot!"

A BACKWARD LOOK

WHEN your Book Comrade led you through the world of Nature, he told you to keep your eyes wide open, your ears alert. If you did so, you saw wonderful sights and learned many secrets of the Out-of-Doors.

The poets and story-tellers told you to look with curious and eager eyes at even the smallest animal, bird, and flower, until you saw many interesting things that a careless glance would never notice. When you watched Bunnyboy in the woods, Mishook in his forest home, and the brood of baby partridges, you saw how woodland mothers teach their children to protect themselves in field and forest. What do you know about the birds and animals that live near your home? How many of them can you name? In what kind of homes do they live?

After listening to what the poets and story-tellers have told you, do you feel a greater love for the Out-of-Doors? Perhaps you would like to make the prayer, "For All Little Birds," your very own; then memorize these lines. It would be fun to build bird houses and put up feeding shelves for the birds.

This Book Comrade can tell you only a few of the many interesting secrets of Nature. Have you learned any other interesting secrets of Nature? On page 369 you will find the names of some other Book Comrades with whom you can go into the Out-of-Doors.

PART · II

LITTLE AMERICAN CITIZENS

FLAGS

Flags of every size
  Float above our land,
The great big one upon the pole
  And a small one in my hand.

The large flag speaks for liberty,
  But the little one does, too;
And it doesn't matter if large or small,
  If it's Red and White and Blue.

And it doesn't matter if large or small,
  The people will understand;
Whether it waves from the steeple
  Or only from my hand.

—Annette Wynne

Reprinted by permission from *For Days and Days: A Year-round Treasury of Verse for Children*, by Annette Wynne. Copyright, 1919, by Frederick A. Stokes Company.

YOU CAN HELP YOUR COUNTRY

Did you read the name of this Part? What is it? Do you know what the word "citizen" means? It means "a person who lives in a country and belongs to it." So, you are a citizen of the United States of America. It is your country. It protects you and gives you many things to make you happy. But your country cannot be great and free and happy unless its boys and girls do their part.

Perhaps you think you have to wait until you are grown up before you can help your country. But this is not true. When you play games hard and fairly, study your lessons faithfully, and help about the home cheerfully, you are doing your part as an American citizen. You are doing your everyday jobs just as well as you can, and that is what your country needs of you.

Now your Book Comrade will tell you some stories of boys and girls—true citizens. You will first be taken far back to the days when our country was young. Here your Book Comrade will tell you of brave Anne Randolph, of unselfish Sally, and of quick-thinking Jonathan Bartlett.

Then your Book Comrade will bring you down to our own times. Perhaps you will want to have a Good Citizen Club. Read these stories to see if you would want some of these people to belong to your club.

ANNE RANDOLPH, A BRAVE AMERICAN GIRL

Author Unknown

Long, long ago, our country fought a war to win freedom from England, for at that time England owned America. This was called the Revolutionary War. During those years of suffering, American boys and girls many times showed that they were brave and true. This story tells of a girl who did a brave thing in order to save her pet cow from the English soldiers.

At the time of the Revolutionary War, a brave little American girl named Anne Randolph lived on a farm not far from Philadelphia. Her father and her two brothers had joined the American army, that was led by General George Washington. Anne and her mother were left alone to take care of the farm.

Two years before the time of this story Anne's father had given her a beautiful calf, and the two had become great friends. Whenever Anne went into the field, the young cow came to be petted.

At one time during the war the English army was in Philadelphia. The soldiers, as they marched through the country, took the farmers' horses and cattle. One day the soldiers came to the farm of

Mr. Randolph. When they saw Anne's pet cow, they tied a rope about her horns and led her away. Anne begged very hard for her pet, but the soldiers only laughed at her.

It did not take long for Anne to think what to do. She ran to the barn, jumped on her pony, and galloped away to see Lord Cornwallis, the general of the English army. It was a very brave thing for a little girl only ten years old to do.

A soldier was on guard in front of the house in which the general was living. "What do you want?" he asked Anne, as she galloped up.

"I must see Lord Cornwallis," she said.

The soldier let her pass, for he thought that she had very important news to tell. When Anne hurried into the room, Lord Cornwallis and some of his friends were at dinner.

"What do you want, my child?" he asked.

"I want my cow, sir. Your soldiers have taken her away, and I have come to get her. Oh, please, sir, you must let me have her."

"And who are you, my little girl?" asked the general, kindly.

"I am Anne Randolph, and I live three miles from here with my mother. Have you seen my cow, sir?"

"Have you no father or brothers, Anne?"

"Yes, sir, I have a father and two brothers, but they are in the army."

"In which army?"

"In the American army, sir."

"Oho! so they are rebels, are they?"

"Oh, yes, sir, we are all rebels here, sir."

"And are you a little rebel yourself?"

"Yes, indeed; I was born a rebel."

The general threw back his head and laughed. "And your cow is a rebel, too, I suppose."

"I think so, sir. She is the nicest cow I ever knew."

The general and his friends laughed again. "Look here, my little rebel," said Lord Cornwallis, "don't you know that we are here to fight the rebels?"

"Yes, sir, but you are not here to fight a little American girl," Anne answered. "Oh, sir," she went on, "I raised my cow myself. She has always been mine. She can't belong to you. I would never steal your cow, sir," the little girl said proudly.

The general rose. "Come here, my child. I promise you that your cow shall be safe in your barn tomorrow; and here, take these," he said, unfastening a pair of silver knee-buckles. "Keep them to remember me by. And if the soldiers trouble your cow again, come to me at once."

ANNE RANDOLPH, A BRAVE AMERICAN GIRL

"Gentlemen," said Lord Cornwallis to his friends, after Anne had left, "this country is certain to be free, with such brave little rebels in it."

The next morning Anne's cow was once more in her own snug barn.

NOTES AND QUESTIONS

1. Which of these three was the bravest thing Anne did?
    (a) She begged the soldiers not to take her cow.
    (b) She asked General Cornwallis to give the cow back.
    (c) She told the general that her father and brothers were fighting against him, and that she was a rebel, too.
2. Which sentence below best tells what this story is about?
    (a) This story tells about a girl whose cow was stolen by some soldiers.
    (b) This is the story of an American girl who went to the general of the English army to get back her pet cow that his soldiers had stolen.
    (c) This story tells about a girl of Revolutionary days, whose cow was stolen by the English soldiers.
3. What two things did General Cornwallis do that showed he liked Anne?
4. Did General Cornwallis think the Americans would win their freedom? What made him think so?
5. Did the general joke a little with Anne? Be ready to read or tell something that proves your answer.

Two other good stories of boys and girls of the early days in our country are "The Powder Candle," Butterworth (in *Child-Library Readers, Book Four*); and "The Pink Tulip," Bailey (in *Boys and Girls of Colonial Days*).

SALLY'S SASH

Grace Kirkpatrick

When Sally put on her new dress with its beautiful white sash, she did not dream that the sash would soon be cut to pieces. This story will tell you why she gave up her sash, and was happy to do so.

One summer day in 1777 a little American girl was jumping up and down, all excited. The little girl was Sally Langdon; this was her birthday, and her mother had just given her a big package.

"Oh, Mother, Mother, is this the package that came from England?" asked the little girl.

"Yes, dear, it is your birthday gift," Mrs. Langdon replied, kissing her little daughter's happy face.

Sally hoped that she would find in the package a pretty silk dress with a white sash, for that was what she wanted most of all.

Her fingers were all trembly as she unfastened the wrappings. Then suddenly, there it was, just as she had hoped it would be, a beautiful silk dress with tiny pink rosebuds all over it, and a sash—white and wide and shiny!

"Oh, please, Mother, may I slip it on and run

to Caroline Chandler's to show it to the girls? They are all over there sewing."

"Yes, dear. There—it looks beautiful." Sally had quickly slipped into her new dress and tied the lovely sash around her waist. "Be careful not to get any spots on it. The girls are coming home to supper with Mary, and another guest will be here, too, a very important one."

Sally skipped happily down the street to Caroline's home. Mrs. Chandler opened the door and told Sally to go into the parlor. At the entrance to the room Sally stopped so quietly that the busy sewers did not see her.

Scattered all about the parlor were pieces of silk, and on a chair was a strip from Mary's best red dress, which had been cut into pieces.

Sally heard her sister Mary say, "Girls, what shall we do? Every bit of white silk is gone, and we must make some more stars. And we must finish it this afternoon, because the Captain is coming to our house for supper tonight!"

Then Sally understood. Spread out before them was a flag that the girls were making—red and white and blue. Our country was very young in those days, and Congress had just decided on a new American flag. It was to have thirteen red and white stripes. Up in one corner, on a field of blue, were to be thirteen white stars. The girls were making one of these new American flags from their silk dresses.

And the Captain? Sally knew that it must be the great Captain John Paul Jones, for his ship had just sailed into the harbor. Everybody was talking about the glorious victories he had won over the English warships. Yes, it must be Captain Jones who was coming to supper—her mother had said there would be an important guest.

"Oh, we must find some more white silk!" cried Caroline.

SALLY'S SASH

"Would—would my sash do?" said Sally, coming quickly into the room.

"Oh, Sally, where did you come from?" exclaimed Mary. "How nice you look! Is that the birthday dress Mother told me about?"

"Yes," answered Sally, "but I will be glad to give the sash to make stars for the flag."

She loved her beautiful silk sash, but she wanted to help as the older girls were doing. With shining eyes she watched the girls' quick fingers cut the ribbon into stars and sew them on the field of blue.

"And now it's done!" cried Caroline. "Sally, aren't you proud that you gave your sash?"

"We shall have to hurry home," said Mary. "Mother will be waiting for us, and perhaps the Captain has already come."

When the excited girls reached the Langdon home with the new flag, Captain Jones was sitting before the fire. He rose and bowed as the girls entered. Then Mary held out the beautiful flag. "Captain Jones," she said, "we have made this new flag for your ship. We shall be honored if you will take it."

"I am deeply thankful to you, my friends," said the brave Captain. "Wherever my ship goes, she will always carry this bonny flag you have made for us."

The next day all the girls were very happy. For Captain Jones invited them to come on board his ship so that they might see the lovely flag raised high in the air.

When Sally came home from the ship, she took out her rosebud dress and put it on. How pretty it looked even without the white silk ribbon! She knew she would always love to wear it and think that the stars made from her sash were sailing far away on the ship of Captain Jones.

Notes and Questions

1. When Sally gave up her sash to make the flag, was she brave, kind-hearted, or unselfish?
2. Why did the girls have to make a flag instead of buying it at a store?
3. For whom was the flag being made?
4. What part of the flag did Sally's sash make?
5. How many stars and stripes were on the first flag?
6. (a) How many stars are there on our flag today?
   (b) How many stripes?
   (c) What do the stars stand for?
   (d) What do the stripes stand for?

You would enjoy reading "The Little Boy Who Became a Great Sailor," "The Old Flag Forever," Stanton, and "The Magic Flag," Paine (all in *Child-Library Readers, Book Four*).

THE SONG OF THE FLAG

Lydia Avery Coonley Ward

Out on the breeze
O'er land and seas,
A beautiful banner is streaming,
Shining its stars,
Splendid its bars,
Under the sunshine 'tis gleaming.
Hail to the flag,
The dear, bonny flag—
The flag that is red, white, and blue.

Over the brave
Long may it wave,
Peace to the world ever bringing,
While to the stars,
Linked with the bars,
Hearts will forever be singing:
Hail to the flag,
The dear, bonny flag—
The flag that is red, white, and blue.

JONATHAN BARTLETT, A PIONEER LAD

Edward W. Frentz

When our country was young, there were hundreds of miles of thick forests and wide plains without a road, a farm, or a city. Boys and girls in those times faced many dangers from Indians and wild animals. You will now read of the strange way in which a boy of those days saved himself from savage wolves.

CROSSING THE PLAINS

Long ago, when our country was young, thirty or more families started to cross the great plains of the West. They wanted to make new homes for themselves where land was free and the farming was easier. One of these families had a five-year-old son, whose name was Jonathan Bartlett.

Jonathan and his mother and father and all the rest of the people traveled in covered wagons. Each wagon was pulled by two or three pairs of oxen. All together the families made up a procession nearly half a mile long.

Under the wagons hung the kettles and pots and pans in which the travelers cooked their meals by the camp fires. All day long the kettles and pans went cling! clang! clang! tink! tank! as they struck against one another.

Sometimes the families slept in the big wagons; but when the weather was pleasant, they spread their blankets on the ground. Then they backed the wagons into a ring about the camp. The men took turns in keeping awake to watch for Indians, and to see that wolves did not get the cattle.

Often after supper, as the travelers sat by the blazing camp fire, a sound would rise from somewhere beyond the ring of wagons. It made the children feel so creepy that they would snuggle close to their fathers. This noise was a wild howl, sometimes coming from one side, and sometimes from the other. Soon another howl just like it would begin, and then another, until there were more howls than one could count. The children would shiver and were glad when someone stirred up the fire.

Jonathan Bartlett's family were taking their dog Shep with them to the new land. It was funny to see old Shep when the howling began. The first time he heard it, he barked with all his might and rushed out into the darkness. In a few minutes back he rushed, whining, with his tail between his legs.

HOW JONATHAN WAS LOST AND SAVED

One evening the families stopped for the night quite early, because they had found a good spring of water. It was Jonathan's fifth birthday, and he was happy over a whistle which one of the men had made for him from the leg-bone of an antelope.

It was still daylight when the travelers stopped, and the little boy took his whistle and went off by himself. He walked such a long way that when he turned to go back, he could not see the camp or hear any voices. But he knew that the wagons could not be far away; so he kept walking.

By and by the sun dropped out of sight, and it began to grow dark, but still there was no camp

JONATHAN BARTLETT, A PIONEER LAD

to be seen. The five-year-old boy was tired and hungry, and he began to grow frightened. So he sat down in a little hollow place in the prairie and cried; but no one came, for no one heard him. And then, after what seemed to him a long time, it began to be light again. The great round moon was peeping over the edge of the hollow in which he sat.

Something else was peeping over the edge of the hollow—something that looked like old Shep. The little boy called to him, "Come, Shep! Nice doggy! Nice old Shep!" But the animal did not come. Instead, it stood up, looked at Jonathan, and backed away. The little boy stood up, too, and started to run toward it. The strange dog did not wait, as Shep would have done; he turned and slipped away. In a few minutes he was back again, sitting where he had sat before. A little to one side of him sat another animal just like him.

Jonathan put the whistle to his lips and blew hard. Both of the strange animals jumped so quickly that they almost fell over backward, and ran off a little way.

That made the boy laugh, and he blew again, and then waited to see what would happen. One of the animals soon came back, sat down again on the edge of the hollow, and watched the little boy. The full moon, shining on the animal's eyes, made them look big and green.

In a few minutes the other animal returned also, and sat down beside the first one. Then others came, until there were five.

And then, all at once they began to make the long, loud howl that Jonathan had so often heard as he sat by the cozy camp fire. He saw that the animals held their heads high in the air, with their noses pointed to the sky. They were singing the song which had made him feel so creepy that he would snuggle up to his father. He knew, then, that they were not dogs, but prairie wolves!

The frightened boy started to cry, but the whistle was in his mouth, and he made only a funny little noise. The wolves stopped their queer singing and jumped. Jonathan blew again, this time with all his might. The animals ran back a few steps. Once more the boy sounded his whistle in a long, high squeal. Then, almost before he knew it, the wolves had gone, and he saw some lights and heard the cries of men and the sound of galloping horses. Down the side of the hollow, bounding and barking, came Shep

85

himself. The next thing Jonathan knew he was in his father's arms and galloping back to camp.

Notes and Questions

1. Which sentence best tells what this story is about?
   (a) This story tells how a boy who was lost on the plains saved himself from wolves by frightening them away with a whistle.
   (b) This story tells of a boy who was lost on the plains.
   (c) This story tells how a boy saved himself from some wolves.

2. Here is a list of the main parts of this story. But the parts are not in the right order. Put them in the right order so that you could use them to tell the story.
   (a) How Jonathan was saved.
   (b) How Jonathan was lost.
   (c) How the pioneers traveled across the plains.
   (d) How Jonathan frightened the wolves.
   (e) How the pioneers camped at night.

3. What shows that even though Jonathan was frightened, he was quick to think and to see a way out of his danger?

4. Have you ever been lost? How did you find your way home or to your parents?

5. Do you know the meaning of *pioneer* and of *prairie*? Don't forget to use your Glossary.

Other good stories are "Traveling in the Old Days," Evans (in *Child-Library Readers, Book Four*); and "The Little Minute Man," Paine (in *Strange Stories of the Revolution,* Pyle and Others).

HOW ANDY HELPED HIS TEAM

Iris May Knight

Andy, the boy in this story, was loyal to his team. So, when he found a way to help the team win the roller-skating race, he did what every loyal boy and girl would do. But it meant giving up something that he greatly wanted for himself.

ANDY'S NEW NEIGHBOR

"Hello, hello!" called out a pleasant voice.

Andy Waters looked up and saw his new neighbor, Francis Frame.

"Hello, yourself," he shouted cheerfully, as he fastened on his roller-skates. "Want to go skating, Francis?"

"I can't. I lost my roller skates last fall, and Mother says she can't afford to buy me another pair just now."

Andy looked at his neighbor's long legs. They were just the right kind, he thought, to make a fast skater.

"That's hard luck, Francis, because if you had some roller-skates, maybe you could be in our skating race next Saturday."

"Skating race? What's that?"

"You see," explained Andy, "the boys in our block are going to have a roller-skating race. We've divided into two teams, and there are about five boys on each side. One team is called the Sunnysiders, because they live on the sunny side of this street. The other team is called the Shadysiders, because they live on the shady side. I'm a Sunnysider."

"Oh! Don't I wish I had some skates!" cried Francis.

"You see," Andy went on, "the losing team has to treat the winning team to a 'wiener' roast afterwards. I'll have to go now. We're meeting in the vacant lot on the corner to talk over some plans. I'll let you use my skates sometime when I am not using them."

Andy skated slowly toward the end of the block. It was a shame, he thought, about Francis Frame. He hadn't lived in the block very long, and none of the other boys knew him. So the new boy was left to himself a great deal, and must often be very lonely.

"Yes," said Andy to himself, "it certainly is a shame about Francis! I ought to do something about it."

As he skated to the vacant lot on the corner, he was met by the captain of the Sunnysiders, a large boy called Buddy Bowers.

"It's time you got here! We were just going to start without you."

"I stopped for a few moments to talk to my new neighbor," said Andy. "Say, Buddy, don't you think we could use another boy on our team? That new boy, Francis Frame, I mean?"

"No, we can't use any more boys, Andy. Besides, he doesn't belong in our gang."

"He looked sort of lonesome—"

"We just can't do it. The Shadysiders only have five on their team, and they wouldn't let us take on an extra boy."

"I hadn't thought of that," Andy replied. "No, we couldn't have more on our team than the Shadysiders have."

Every afternoon the sound of skating was heard on both sides of Pine Street. Andy practiced very hard, for his heart was set on having the Sunnysiders win the race. Still, he couldn't help knowing that his short legs kept him from being a fast skater. Once Buddy had said to him, "Those Shadysiders have some good skaters on their team. We'll have to go like the wind to beat them. Can't you skate a little faster, Andy?"

ANDY MAKES A PLAN

Just then Francis Frame came out to the sidewalk and watched the Sunnysiders skate past. Somehow it made Andy feel uncomfortable, for he remembered his promise to let Francis use his skates.

"After this race is over, I'll let him use them all he wants to," he said to himself. "And I'll see that he gets a chance to play with the other boys in this block."

Suddenly Andy stopped skating. He had thought of a way to help his team win, and also to help Francis Frame.

HOW ANDY HELPED HIS TEAM

"But I don't want to do it," he said to himself. "It's too late to do anything about it now, and besides, he probably can't skate much. He has long legs, but I don't believe he has any muscle."

Andy went to bed that night still trying to decide what he would do. The next day was Friday, and when he awoke in the morning, he was still thinking about the race.

Buddy stopped for him on the way to school, and all that the two boys talked about was the race.

"Do you really think we can win?" asked Andy.

"Of course," Buddy replied. "We just have to win. The Shadysiders beat us last year, but we're not going to let them do it again."

Suddenly Andy knew just what he was going to do. Even though he wasn't a fast skater, he could help his team win the race. And at the same time he could help Francis make some friends in the neighborhood. Andy could hardly wait for school to close.

Finally three o'clock came, and he skated as fast as he could to the home of his new neighbor.

"Hello," Francis called. "How's everything?"

"I have something important to talk over with you," said Andy. "But first, would you like to use my roller-skates for a while?"

"Would I?" cried Francis in a delighted voice.

Andy watched Francis as he sped toward the corner. It was true that the new boy did not seem to have much muscle, but his legs were long, and they carried him to the corner and back in a surprisingly short time.

"It surely is fun to be on skates again!" said Francis happily.

"How would you like to take my place in the race tomorrow?" Andy asked suddenly.

"What do you mean?" said Francis, looking very much surprised.

"You see," answered Andy, "you're a faster skater than I am. My legs are too short. The Sunnysiders just have to win this race, and if you take my place, our team is more likely to win. I'll let you use my skates, and you might practice a while this afternoon."

"What will your captain say?"

"I'll make it all right with him. It's for the good of the team."

"All right," Francis said slowly, "if you're sure you want me to do it. You don't know whether I'm any good. The team would be pretty sore at you if I didn't do very well."

"You never mind that," replied Andy quickly.

HOW ANDY HELPED HIS TEAM

"I know you can help us win. I'll stop by for you in the morning."

"I'll be ready," Francis promised.

AN EXCITING RACE

Saturday morning at ten o'clock nearly all of the boys who were to be in the race were at their meeting-place, the vacant lot on Pine Street. Each Sunnysider wore a yellow band around his left arm, and each Shadysider wore a brown band. Mr. Thompson, the physical director of the school, who was to be the umpire, had already come. A big crowd of boys and girls was standing around, waiting to see the race.

"Why isn't Andy here?" asked Buddy. "We're going to start in a few minutes. Tom, you run to his house and see what's wrong."

Just then Andy and Francis came hurrying up.

"Buddy, I'm not going to skate," Andy began, quietly. "Francis is going to take my place."

"What's the matter, Andy? Hurt yourself?"

"No, but I've decided not to skate in this race."

Buddy and all the other Sunnysiders looked surprised.

"Lost your nerve, did you?" called out one of the boys.

Andy's face grew red. "No, I didn't!" he answered, "but I'm not going to skate in this race. Francis Frame is going to take my place. He's a better skater than I am."

Buddy took Andy aside. "That new boy can't skate. You're just giving the race away to the Shadysiders. Come on and take your place," begged the captain.

"You just wait and see if he can't skate!" Andy exclaimed. "I know he'll help win the race. Anyway, I'm not going to skate."

Just then Mr. Thompson shouted, "First skaters, come to the starting-place. It's time to begin."

Each Sunnysider was lined up with a member of the other team who was about his own size, for only two boys were to race at a time. The first two boys took their places at the starting-point. Then Mr. Thompson blew the whistle.

At first the brown-banded boy took the lead, but the yellow-banded boy was not far behind. When they reached the turn at the other end of the block, the Sunnysider began to gain on the other skater. Faster and faster he went, while all the boys and girls shouted. A moment later he darted across the finish line ten feet ahead of the boy with the brown band.

At the end of four rounds, each team had won two victories. The fifth round would decide the race, and Francis Frame was the fifth skater for the Sunnysiders.

"Don't forget that I'm counting on you. I know you can do it," Andy said, as Francis took his place at the starting-point.

The Shadysider who was to skate against Francis was about the same size as the new boy, though his legs were a little longer.

For the fifth time that morning came the starting-signal.

"On your mark!" cried Mr. Thompson.

"Get ready!"

The whistle blew!

At first Francis dashed ahead and held the lead. How all the Sunnysiders did cheer and shout! But suddenly they gave a groan. Somehow Francis had slipped, and now lay flat on the sidewalk.

The Shadysider darted quickly ahead, and by the time Francis was on his feet again, was far in the lead.

"Go it, old man!" shouted Andy. "You can beat him yet!"

Then the Sunnysiders gave a cheer. Francis was slowly creeping up on the boy with the brown band. At last the end of the block was reached. Both skaters had made the turn and were racing back toward their cheering teams. The Shadysider was still ahead, but Francis kept gaining on him until the two were side by side.

Now they were near the end of the race. Every boy in the crowd was shouting, but Andy's excited voice was heard above all the others.

"You can do it! You can do it! You can do it!"

Francis put all his strength into the last few yards and crossed the goal just ahead of the boy with the brown band.

HOW ANDY HELPED HIS TEAM

The Sunnysiders had won. Francis Frame would no longer be the "new boy" in the block. And Andy was the happiest boy in all the crowd.

"My legs may be too short for me to be a fast skater," he said to himself, "but just the same, my skates won the race."

Notes and Questions

1. (a) What was Andy's first reason for wanting Francis on his team? (b) What was the reason that finally made Andy put him on the team?

2. Below are three reasons Andy gave to himself for not letting Francis be on the team. Which was the real reason, and which were just excuses?

    (a) "It's too late to do anything now."
    (b) "He probably can't skate much."
    (c) "I don't want to do it."

3. If Francis had failed, how would the boys have felt toward Andy?

4. Why did it take courage for Andy to make the boys let Francis take his place?

Two other good stories are "Chums," Ames (in *Child-Library Readers, Book Four*); and "An Airplane Stowaway," Bunn (in *Child Life,* October, 1931).

SAFETY FIRST IN THE CITY

Benjamin Veit

Stop! Look! Listen! Did you ever see those words on a sign at a railroad crossing? They are good words to remember in these days of swift automobiles, street cars, and trains. You may sometime have to do a dangerous thing, but to put yourself carelessly in the way of danger is foolishness, not bravery. Our country needs strong and healthy boys and girls. Be careful!

"WHAT IS TRAFFIC?"

After a happy ride of three hours, George Benton reached the city for his first visit. As he stepped off the train in the midst of the hurrying crowd, he looked about for his Uncle Robert and Cousin Arthur. Suddenly he saw them on another platform.

"Hello, Arthur!" shouted George, starting to run across the two tracks that were between him and his relatives.

"Hold on there, George!" cried his uncle. "Don't cross those tracks. There's an engine coming. Just walk straight ahead to the gate, and we'll meet you there. We got on the wrong platform."

SAFETY FIRST IN THE CITY 99

A few minutes later George joined his uncle and cousin at the gate.

"Well, George," said Uncle Robert, "we're glad to see you. Arthur will show you a good time, and will try to teach you as many interesting things about the city as you taught him about the country last summer. But first of all, you will need to learn what we all try to learn in the city—to be very careful. If you had crossed the tracks where you got off, you might have met with an accident."

"Oh, I'll look out for George, Father," said Arthur. "You've taught me how to take care of myself, and ever since Willie Barnes got hurt by a street car, I've been mighty careful. George, I've got a fine program of sight-seeing and fun planned for you—there will be something doing all the time."

"I think I know how to look out for myself, Uncle Robert, even if I am from the country," said George.

"It isn't only country boys, George, who must keep their eyes open in the city," replied his uncle. "Boys born and brought up in the city, and grown-ups, too, must look where they are going. Some of us find we can't always escape danger even when we are careful. You'll soon get used to the city, but no matter how long you are here, you will always find that it pays to be on the safe side. 'Safety First' is our motto, George, in these days of heavy street traffic."

"What's traffic?" George asked Arthur, as the boys walked through the station just ahead of Mr. Wilson.

"Why," explained Arthur, "that means the wagons and street cars and automobiles and trucks and things like that, all moving here and there among the crowds of people who are crossing from one sidewalk to the other. Street traffic is what causes the danger to people who are walking. It seems to be getting worse every year. You have to watch your step pretty carefully."

"BETTER SAFE THAN SORRY"

Mr. Wilson and the boys stood at the corner waiting for the street car that would take them home. Cars were passing in four directions, and the clanging of gongs and the noise of wheels on the tracks sounded very loud in the ears of the country boy.

"Oh!" cried Uncle Robert, suddenly. "There has been an accident."

He was pointing to a woman who had tried to step down from a street car, while facing backward. She had fallen in the street and her bundles were scattered all around her. George saw a man dart from the crowd and help her to her feet. Luckily the woman was not injured, but the fall had given her a bad fright.

"Many people get off the wrong way, George," said his uncle. "If they could only learn always to face forward when getting off the car, there wouldn't be so many accidents. If you get off facing backward and the car starts before you have your feet firmly planted on the street, you will get a fall nearly every time. It's almost impossible to keep your feet when you are jerked backward. But, if you face forward, in the direction the car is going, you can almost always keep from falling even if the car starts before you get your footing."

It was all new to George, and all very interesting. He said to himself that he would remember that lesson and never face backward when getting off a street car.

The car for which Uncle Robert and the boys were waiting came along and stopped. They all stepped into the street to get on, but the car was very crowded. George made a dash for the platform and swung on, holding to the rod with one hand, while he carried his traveling bag in the other. He could find room for only one foot on the lower step.

"Better wait for the next car, George," said Uncle Robert. "One will be along in a minute or two, and it may not be so crowded." He helped the boy down from the step just as the car started ahead.

"A few minutes' time doesn't matter so much as getting thrown down and injured," said Uncle Robert. "Many people fall from crowded cars, and sometimes are run over by automobiles before

SAFETY FIRST IN THE CITY

they can get up again. It is better to be safe than sorry."

The next car was not so crowded, and they all found seats for the ride to the Wilson home. When it was time to get off, George remembered the accident that had happened to the woman. He stepped down from the car very carefully, facing forward instead of backward. In a few minutes they were safely home, and the country boy thought that he had already learned a good deal about the dangers of the big city.

HOW TO TAKE CARE OF YOURSELF IN THE CITY

The next day the boys were up bright and early. After a good breakfast they talked over the program for the day.

"I think we had better just take a walk this morning," Arthur said, "so that you can see how things look. Everything will be new to you. We'll take a street car down town and walk around where the big stores and the tall office buildings are. They call these buildings skyscrapers, because they are so high."

When the car had reached the street at which they were to get off, both boys stepped from the platform with their faces toward the front. Then

George started to cross the street, just behind the car.

"Wait a minute," said Arthur. "Stand right here in the middle of the street until our car gets out of the way, so that we can see what is coming. Look! There's a car coming right in our direction, and it might have hit us if we had started to cross the street without looking. If you want to keep from being run down by a street car that is moving in the other direction from the one you have just left, you must always look both ways before starting to cross the street."

SAFETY FIRST IN THE CITY

After the way was clear, the boys walked quickly to the sidewalk, and turned to watch the street traffic. What a different sight it was from the quiet country roads! It was the hour when thousands of men and women were going to their places of work. The sidewalks were crowded with hurrying people. The streets were full of automobiles and heavy trucks and clanging cars.

As George looked at the strange sight in the busy city, he said to his cousin, "My! I wonder how so many people can cross these crowded streets without being run over."

"Well, George," said Arthur, "a good many people do get run over. Almost every day the papers tell of accidents. It isn't easy to take care of yourself. And of course the smaller children don't know the danger. We older ones ought to watch out for them. Just look there— see that girl warning two little children not to cross behind the car! She stopped them just in time."

"So this is what you call street traffic?" said George. "Well, I don't wonder that Mother told me to be very careful."

"That's just what my mother told me when I visited you last summer in the country," laughed

Arthur. "Let's walk along a little, and look around."

The boys walked slowly to the middle of the block, where they stopped to watch a crowd on the sidewalk.

"Hello! what's up?" cried Arthur.

A tall policeman darted from the crowd and ran out into the street, where there was a tangle of wagons and cars. A man who had tried to walk across the street in the middle of the block had been knocked down by a wagon.

"He should have known better," said Arthur. "Always cross the street at the corner, and you'll stand a much better chance of getting through safely."

George was very tired when he got home from the first day's sight-seeing, but he had learned a great deal about taking care of himself in the city.

Before the end of his visit, George Benton had seen so many narrow escapes from injury in the city streets that he had become very careful. But his carefulness did not make his visit any less interesting to him.

And when he went back to his home in the country, he had many things to tell about the

SAFETY FIRST IN THE CITY

city. The thing he liked best to talk about was the busy traffic and how he had learned to take care of himself even when the streets were full of cars, automobiles, trucks, and wagons.

NOTES AND QUESTIONS

1. Why are city streets such dangerous places?
2. What does "Safety First" mean?
3. When a person steps off a street car, should he face backward or forward?
4. Why should you wait for the street car to go on before crossing behind it?
5. Where is the safest place to cross a street?
6. If you know of any accidents, tell why they happened.
7. Tell of some other ways in which a person may be careful, as for example, with fire and electricity, in swimming, and when riding a bicycle.

A BACKWARD LOOK

Do you remember what General Cornwallis said to his friends after Anne had left? He said that he was sure America would win its freedom, because it had such brave young citizens as Anne Randolph. He was right, as you know.

Which story in this Part did you like best? Why did you like it? Were there any boys and girls whom you would want in your Good Citizen Club? In one of these stories you learned some important things that everyone should know. Which one was it?

In these stories there were probably some things that you did not understand very well. For example, do you know who Captain John Paul Jones was? It would be interesting to read about some of the great things he did. Who made the first Stars and Stripes? Where in our country are the Great Plains across which the covered wagons traveled? Why did so many people leave their homes and travel far across our country? Can you make a picture of a covered wagon with its teams of oxen?

Perhaps you have read some other stories of boys and girls at work and at play. Be ready to tell the class a good story you have read. If you want to read more stories like the ones in this Part, turn to pages 369-370. There you will find the names of some books that you will enjoy.

PART · III

BOYS AND GIRLS OF OTHER LANDS

EVERY CHILD OF EVERY LAND

Let every child of every land
   Join hands in this glad game,
For though our speech may different be,
   Our laughter is the same.

For though our speech may different be,
   The same sun shines on all,
And loves to see all children glad
   That live on this green ball.

—S. Winsten

EVERY LAND HAS ITS LITTLE CITIZENS

EVERY land has its little citizens—boys and girls who are playing games, learning their lessons, and helping their parents. It would be fun if you could run over some afternoon or Saturday and play with these boys and girls of far-away lands. They would have many interesting things to tell you and show you, and you could tell them just as many interesting things about your country. Many of their ways of living would seem very queer to you, but some of the things you do would seem just as strange to them.

Perhaps you will some day be able to travel to far-away lands; it may be that you will never be able to do so. But in the pages of books you can always take a journey. You may visit places where very few people have ever gone. You will learn things that it has taken people many years to learn. One of the stories you are now going to read was written by a woman who lived many years in China. Of course she learned more about China than you could learn in a short visit. Another story tells of a journey made by a little girl through a part of Africa where few white people have ever been.

You will enjoy the four stories in this Part of your book. As you go traveling in them, you will see that these boys and girls of far-away lands are much like the boys and girls you know.

ALICE TRAVELS IN JUNGLELAND

Mary Hastings Bradley

This is a true story of Alice Bradley, whose home is in Chicago. Her father and mother went to Africa with some friends to study the animals and people of the strange and beautiful land. Alice went with them on their travels. This story tells you how they marched from day to day, and of the black men, called "boys," who carried their baggage.

WHAT THE TRAVELERS CARRIED

It made Alice laugh to see how many things a white man needed in Africa: his tent, his cot and blankets, his clothing, his folding-chairs and tables, his guns and bullets, his cameras, his food-boxes and cooking-pans and medicines.

The black man traveled with just the goatskin that he wore day and night, his spear, his knife, his gourd for water, and a little bag in which he carried his pipe and tobacco and a little food.

A strong black man can take sixty pounds on his head and walk with it from four to eight hours a day. It took two hundred black men to carry all the things that this party of six people needed in the jungle. They had sixty-five boxes of food alone! And the matches they carried were nearly enough to make a full load for one porter. The natives made fire by twirling a piece of very hard wood in a hole in a piece of very soft wood. With just a few twirls they made a spark glow in the soft wood.

The part of Africa in which Alice was traveling is so high and mountainous that the nights are cold, although the sun is hot in the daytime. At the end of a day's march the natives built huts of grass, into which they crowded to keep warm. Often they built fires in the grass huts at night. Sometimes a hut caught on fire and flamed up like a huge bonfire, but the people inside jumped through the flames in an instant.

Now Alice was really on *safari;* that means *on the march.* The party was traveling straight north through the mountains of central Africa, marching every day, and camping every night.

Alice lived, during camping hours, in a green linen tent either with her mother or Priscilla, her nurse; she slept on a cot which could be folded up into a bag. The little girl had green linen bags in which were carried her clothes and bedding, her wash-basin, and her fold-up linen bathtub. In an air-tight tin box she had her most precious belongings: the picture books and beads and paper dolls that had to last her till she was out of the jungle again.

STARTING OUT IN THE MORNING

One *safari* day was like another. Each day began very early in the morning, because the travelers wanted to get most of the marching done before the noon heat overtook them and to make camp before the storms which came early every afternoon. There are only two seasons in Africa, the dry and the wet. As this was the wet season, each afternoon a black storm-cloud would come rolling along, and for a little while there would be a great downpour of rain. After that the sun would come out brightly again.

The African mornings are as black as night, for it is always dark until the sun gets up. Then the light comes all at once, as if you pulled up a window shade and let in the bright sunlight. In central Africa the sun always rises at six in the morning, and sets at six in the evening; so no one in Alice's party needed a watch to tell him the time at sunrise or sunset.

Sometimes at four o'clock in the morning, sometimes even at three, Alice would find herself being pulled out of her warm blankets and hurried into her clothes. The tent was chilly and lighted only by a candle.

The tent boys would come running in with hot water just about the time everybody had had a hurried wash with cold water. Alice would give her hair a hasty brushing, pull on her sweater, and run out to the breakfast table, which was set outside the tents.

Candles would be burning, and in the darkness the boys who helped with the cooking would be running back and forth from the kitchen fire, bringing hot prunes and cereal and toast and bacon and coffee. Behind the breakfast table other boys were putting out the bags and taking down the tents.

Eagerly the natives would watch the white people eat. They had no wish for the white man's food, but, oh, how they watched the big tin cans from which the milk and jam and biscuits came! Whenever a can was tossed away, there was a great rush for it. If you had never had anything for a water jug except a gourd or a pottery bowl that broke very easily, and then suddenly you saw things like cans, that didn't break at all, *you* would rush and scramble for them, too! They would be much more precious than any silly thing like money, that couldn't buy cans in the jungle at all!

After breakfast Alice always trotted off to see if everything she wanted was in her basket: her doll and picture book, her bottle of drinking water, and the lunch that Priscilla always put up for her—cold chicken and crackers and cheese and bananas.

The busiest moment of the morning was just after breakfast, for every porter was trying to get his load on his head and hurry off with it. Uncle Akeley and Father were trying to keep all the two hundred porters together, and not let anybody get away until every load was taken care of. Priscilla was busy getting Alice ready, and Mother and Martha were trying to get the breakfast things back into the boxes.

The boys who helped the cook never would hurry with washing the breakfast dishes; so the boxes that held the dishes were always the last to be ready.

The porters who carried them hoped that some time they would manage to get off with the empty boxes before the dishes were put into them. Every morning they came and sat beside the boxes, waiting for a chance.

So Alice had to sit on guard each morning,

like a little girl shooing off hens; and every time a black arm would reach slyly out for an empty box she would shout, *"Hapana!"* (No). Then there would be a laugh from the black boys. They were always very good-natured about it.

At last every man would have his load, and the long line would be ready. The leaders, rushing ahead, blew their horns, and the porters followed, with the loads on their heads. The Bradleys used to march at the front of the procession, and Uncle Akeley at the end of it. Here he could take pictures without stopping the march, and could see that no loads were dropped. No porter ever stole anything, but sometimes one ran away and left his load in the path.

THE DAY'S MARCH

The sun would be coming up as the procession started, and the white people would pull off their sweaters and throw them on some bundle. Every hour it would grow hotter and hotter, till at noon the sun stood overhead, and your shadow was a huddled little thing just under your feet, like a black kitten trying to get out of the way. Then it would grow cooler and cooler till the sun dropped behind the mountains at six o'clock.

Usually Alice rode in a basket carried by two natives, with two others to change off. She didn't like the basket, but she had to ride many a mile in it over the rough, steep ways. Often she would curl up in her basket and sleep like a kitten. Sometimes at a hill too steep for Alice to be carried in the basket, one of the boys would put her on his shoulders and carry her.

The traveling Alice liked best was to ride on a little seat on the front of a bicycle ridden by one of the native boys. Think of bicycles in Africa! Yet the party had brought six of them, for the paths between native villages have been made so smooth by bare feet that bicycles can often be ridden. When the paths were too steep or rough or muddy after the rains began, the porters carried the bicycles on their heads, as they did not know how to wheel them.

One porter was so afraid of the bicycles that he wouldn't touch them. He thought it was magic that made them go. When he was told to carry one, he lay down on the ground and shook with fear. And yet this man was so brave that he had killed a lion with his spear!

On the march the travelers always sent messengers ahead to tell the chief in the next village that the party was coming with a great number of porters for whom they wanted to buy food. When the party drew near the village, the chief and his men would come out to meet them. The chiefs usually wore skins, strings of beads, and bracelets.

Every native carried his spear in his hand, wherever he went. Once, when Alice and her mother were marching at the head of the procession, they looked up and saw the chief and his men waiting at the top of the hill. When the chief looked down and saw them—saw that a little child was coming—he drove his spear deep into the ground; and all his men did the same. That was their way of saying to the strangers, "It is peace."

The chief always brought a present of a live chicken, which some follower carried, dangling upside down from his wrist. Alice was very sorry for the poor chicken, and she used to see that it had water and food in camp.

The white people would also give the chief a present, usually money. Then the chief would allow the travelers to get water from the nearest river, and would give them firewood; he would also give them eggs and chickens, or whatever other food there was. After this the white people picked out a good place to camp and told the porters to bring in the boxes and bundles.

CAMPING AT NIGHT

The moment the porters got in, they dropped their loads and rushed off to see about getting a sleeping-place in the huts of the village. Sometimes the porters would bring back some of the village men to help set up the tents for the white people and to carry the different bags and boxes to the right places.

As soon as the cook had his tent up and his fire going, he began getting dinner. Sometimes the dinner was at two o'clock, sometimes at four or at six. When dinner was to be late, the travelers would eat the crackers and chocolate they carried in their pockets, and open a bottle of lime juice, which is the finest-tasting thing in the world on a hot day in Africa.

Often the rain would come pouring down just as the meal was ready. If it didn't rain too hard, the cook-boys used to dash from the cooking-tent to the dining-tent with the food. The rain did not often last long, and the sun always came out again.

The native women from the villages used to bring in food for the porters, and lay it out in rows. The food was usually bananas or meal tied in banana leaves. Then the porters would line up, and each man would take what was opposite him and go off and cook it. Sometimes the white people bought oxen for the porters from a chief who had cattle; and sometimes they fed the porters antelope meat.

Before dinner was over Alice was always nodding into her plate, and off she would go with Priscilla to their tent. When the little girl was snuggled down cosily in her blankets, Priscilla would tie the tent flaps shut so that no insect could slip inside, and then go out and join the others in the camp chairs.

Alice would fall asleep hearing the murmur of the white people in front of her tent, and farther away, like a humming of bees, the chatter of the porters about their little fires. The porters never seemed to sleep. They would have laughed and talked all night if the white people had let them. That was the fun they got out of the trip.

They used to shout with laughter over the doings of the white people they were traveling with, over the queer clothes they wore, and the queer way they ate. Alice used to hear the word "*Wazungu*" (Stranger), followed by laughter and song, until Uncle Akeley's shout, "*Pana kilele*" (No noise),

ALICE TRAVELS IN JUNGLELAND

put an end to the fun-making and made everybody settle down for the night.

NOTES AND QUESTIONS

1. To see whether you know how the white people traveled, tell what words belong where the letters are below. Your first answer is (a) *Africa*.

On the journey through ....(a).... the six white people needed ....(b).... native porters to carry their baggage. Each porter carried about ....(c).... pounds, and he carried the load on his ....(d)..... Most of the traveling was done in the ....(e)...., because later in the day it got so ....(f).... and also because it ....(g).... then. When they found paths, they used ....(h).... for traveling. The white people slept in ....(i)...., and the natives slept in ....(j).....

2. Why did the natives want the tin cans so badly?

3. How did the native chiefs show strangers that they wished to meet them peacefully?

4. How do you know from this story that there were no roads in this part of Africa?

5. Tell two things about the porters that show they did not like to work.

6. Be ready to read or tell something in this story that you thought was funny.

7. Explain:
   (a) Alice was always nodding into her plate.
   (b) safari
   (c) gourd
   (d) air-tight

This story was taken from a book named *Alice in Jungleland.* You would enjoy reading it. You would also like *The Magic Doll of Rumania,* by Queen Marie of Rumania, and *Little Folks of Other Lands,* by Piper.

MONI AND HIS GOATS

JOHANNA SPYRI

Moni was a goat boy in Switzerland. In the villages of that country, each family generally keeps a few goats for their milk. Every morning Moni took these goats, with his own, up into the mountains. All day he watched over them while they grazed on the little plots of grass among the rocks and cliffs. The villagers thought that all he had to do was to sing and enjoy himself, but this story shows that he had to be brave and faithful as well.

THE BOY AND HIS HERD

It was very early in the morning when Moni, the goat boy, came through the little Swiss village singing his song. The goats sprang from their sheds to meet him as he waved his switch and called to them.

In the sky the rosy clouds were piled high, and a fresh morning breeze whispered about the ears of Moni as he climbed upward. How pleasant it all was! Everything was the way he liked to have it. The boy sang out of pure happiness; his voice rang far down into the valley, where many a sleeper opened his eyes in surprise, only to close them again as he heard the merry voice of the goat boy.

Moni and the goats climbed upward for about two hours until they were high among the peaks of the mountains. The higher they climbed, the brighter everything seemed. Once more the goat boy began to sing from the bottom of his heart, louder and more joyously the farther up he went. And this is the song that rang out among the mountain peaks:

> Sing, birds, on the high slopes;
> Sing where the fir trees grow.
> Whenever you sing the sun comes out,
> And the rain is sure to go.

Long days and a short night
Come with the summer-time;
And the berries are ripe upon the stem,
And the woods are sweet with thyme.

Nuts grow on the thick hedge;
Autumn is on its way;
And high on the crags the herbs are good,
Where the goats have gone to play.

Moni kept on climbing until he reached a little green mountain meadow. In this spot he often stayed for hours at a time while his animals grazed quietly about him. Sometimes Moni sat on a certain high rock, from which he could see far off through the valley.

Today he took his little sack of bread and cheese from his back and laid it in a small hollow of the ground which he had long ago dug out. Then he threw himself down on the fragrant grass among the yellow rock-roses and purple gentians and looked happily about him.

The sky was now a deep blue. On all sides of Moni were the high mountains with their snow-covered peaks that seemed to reach to the very sky itself. Moni lay whistling joyously, while a pleasant mountain breeze cooled his warm face. If he stopped whistling for a moment, the birds took up the song even more gayly than he, as they flew off into the blue sky. The goat boy was perfectly happy.

From time to time Meggie, the youngest kid, would come up and rub her little head on Moni's shoulder. Then she would give a loving bleat and go around to the other side of the boy and rub against him once more. The rest of the flock came, one after the other, to see the goatherd, and each of the animals had his own way of showing his love for Moni.

When Brownie, Moni's own goat, came for his visit, he walked around the boy very carefully as if he were making sure that everything was just as usual. And he would not go away until Moni said, "Yes, yes, Brownie, everything is all right. Now go back to your grazing."

Then came a young gray goat, and close behind him a white one named Swallow because she was so tiny and quick that she seemed to dart past like a swallow flying to its nest. The young gray goat and Swallow rushed at Moni so excitedly that they would have tumbled him over if he had not already been stretched out on the ground.

As they went racing off again, Meggie's mother, the shiny black goat, who was a little proud, came slowly forward. She stopped a few feet away from the goat boy, as if she did not care to be too friendly, looked at him for a moment, and then went away.

Great Sultan, the oldest and largest of the goats, always came up bleating in a way that seemed to say: "I am the leader of this herd of goats, and have come to talk things over with you." Today as usual he approached Moni proudly, shoving off the goats who were near by. But Meggie would not let herself be crowded away. She huddled under Moni's arm so that the Great Sultan could not reach her.

So the sunny morning passed. Finally Moni sat up and leaned thoughtfully on the staff that he always carried to help him over the rough places. He was wondering if he might try to climb a new side of the mountain this afternoon. It would be fun to lead the goats high up to the Three Dragon Stones, where the tenderest grass and bushes grew. The way was steep, and there were dangerous places on the mountain wall; but he knew a good path, and the goats were always very careful.

HOW MONI SAVED MEGGIE

So, after eating his lunch, Moni started up to the Three Dragon Stones, with the goats climbing joyfully after him. Soon most of them had run ahead of him except little Meggie, who always stayed near at hand. At first everything went very well. With long leaps the goats rushed forward to the green bushes and grass on the slopes above. Ahead of them all ran the light-footed Swallow, springing from rock to rock. Today she was to have a surprise.

Half-way up, the young goat stopped suddenly. Before her stood a wild chamois looking curiously at her. Such a thing had never happened to Swallow before. She stood still, waiting for the stranger to move aside so that she could jump to the rock above. But the wild mountain animal did not stir from Swallow's path; he kept on looking boldly into her eyes.

How long they would have been standing there I do not know, if the Great Sultan had not caught up to them just in time to see what was happening. He passed Swallow carefully and pushed the chamois to one side roughly. Swallow turned her soft eyes to the Great Sultan as if to thank him, and then bounded gayly away.

And now it seemed as if the swift and daring Swallow had set a bad example for the other goats. Some of them began to leap so quickly from rock to rock that Moni had to cry out warningly: "Take it easy! Take it easy! Don't crowd in the steep places, or one of you will be down below in a moment with a broken leg."

Scarcely had the goat boy paused for breath when he cried out again in fright, "Swallow, what has got into your head?" The swift goat had now climbed as high as the Dragon Stones and had bounded up to the very edge of one of them, where she stood looking saucily down at him. Moni moved like lightning in the next few moments. If Swallow should make a single step forward, she would fall many feet below! The boy climbed hurriedly up and drew her back.

"You come down with me, little silly," he scolded.

Moni led Swallow down and held her until she had forgotten all about her desire to run away.

"Where is Meggie?" shouted Moni suddenly as he saw Blackie standing all by herself on the edge of a steep, rocky wall. The young kid was always near her mother if she was not beside Moni. "What have you done with your kid, Blackie?" Moni cried, hurrying to where the goat stood.

The mother goat behaved very strangely. She ate nothing and stood in one spot with her ears pointed as if listening. Moni reached her side and stood listening also. Suddenly he heard a faint bleat. It was Meggie's voice coming up from below, a pitiful and frightened call for help. Moni lay down on the ground and leaned over the edge. Far below there was something moving, and he saw that it was Meggie hanging over the bough of a tree that grew out from the cliff.

"Oh, she must have fallen down!" cried Moni.

Fortunately the branch had caught the little goat, or she would have fallen many feet below. But even now if she could not keep her place, she would fall and be dashed to pieces. In the most anxious tone, Moni called down, "Hold on, Meggie; hold fast to the branch. See, I am coming to get you."

But how could he save the kid that was bleating so piteously below? The mountain wall was so steep that he could not climb down it. Moni thought hard. The little goat must be about on a level with the Rain Cliff, an overhanging rock under which the goat boys gathered for shelter when a mountain storm arose. From that spot Moni thought he could climb upward to the tree on which Meggie was hanging.

Quickly the boy whistled his herd together and led them to a level spot near the Rain Cliff. There he left them to graze and went on by himself to the Cliff. When he looked up at poor Meggie, she seemed to be very high above him. Moni saw that it was going to be hard to reach the young goat, and still harder to climb down again with Meggie on his back. But that was the only way to save the little animal.

So the boy started at once to climb up the cliff until he reached the tree. Then he made his way to the bough on which the frightened little animal hung. Grasping the trembling kid fast in both hands, he raised her to his shoulders, and

MONI AND HIS GOATS

with the greatest care climbed back down. When his feet touched firm earth again and he saw that Meggie was safe, he cried, "Oh, dear God, I thank Thee a thousand times for helping me to save Meggie. How happy we both are!"

Then Moni sat down and stroked the kid, whose delicate limbs still trembled with fright. And when it was time to lead the flock homeward, the goat boy took the kid in his arms, saying tenderly, "Come, poor Meggie, you are still shaking. You can't walk home. I will carry you."

And so he carried the little animal the whole way down, and the villagers who came to get their goats from Moni heard the story and were filled with surprise. They had always thought that the goat boy had nothing to do all day but lie in a cool mountain pasture, singing his songs.

Notes and Questions

1. What did Moni do that showed he was brave?
2. What showed that he was kind-hearted?
3. How do you know that he was a happy boy?
4. Which sentence below best proves that Moni was kind to the goats?
    (*a*) They followed him wherever he went.
    (*b*) They liked to play with him.
    (*c*) He saved Meggie.
5. Would it be easier for goats or for cows to find food in Moni's country? Why?
6. Write these words in a column: *grazed, fragrant, fortunately, cliff, peaks, darted*. Opposite each word write a word or phrase that means the same. Your first answer is *grazed—ate grass*. Your Glossary will help you.
7. Be ready to read or tell the most exciting part of the story.
8. Be ready to read lines that tell of the beauty of Switzerland.
9. Did you know how to pronounce *chamois* and *gentian*?

You would like to read *Moni the Goat Boy,* the book from which this story was taken. Two other good stories are "Shepherd Girl," Miller (in *Children of the Mountain Eagle*); and *The Swiss Twins,* Perkins.

TONINO TAKES HIS POTTERY TO THE FAIR
Helen Hill and Violet Maxwell

Tonino and his sister, Nanou, lived in the little old town of Nouvilo in southeastern France. Many children in Nouvilo decorated pottery for the potter in the next village, but Tonino learned to make, in his own home, cunning little bowls and cups with figures of his pet animals for handles. Nanou painted them in gay colors. Then Mamcto, his grandmother, and Tonino started out with the pottery in the donkey cart for the fair at Vence.

ARRIVING IN VENCE

Vence is a very old city in France. It has towers and city gates and narrow streets just like Nouvilo. Long before Tonino arrived at the outside wall, he could see the cathedral tower sticking up in the middle of the city. All around the old city were rows and rows of houses, white or pink or pale yellow, and with bright red roofs. There was a broad avenue shaded by big trees and with many big hotels.

When they turned into the main street, Tonino was surprised at the shops he saw: a grocery shop with big glass windows, shops with pretty dresses

---

From Hill and Maxwell's *Little Tonino*. By permission of The Macmillan Company, publishers.

in the windows, and a shop where they sold only pencils and paper and paint-boxes and books. There was even a shop where they sold automobiles. Tonino had never imagined anything like it in his life, and he was sure that his little sister, Nanou, would never believe he was telling the truth when he told her all about it.

Soon Tonino and Mameto heard a gay sound of music, and a minute later they were on the Grand Place of Vence, which is about five times as big as the Grand Place at Tonino's home in Nouvilo. The Grand Place was crowded with people, for the big fair was in full swing. There were two merry-go-rounds, one with horses and one with automobiles, and both of them played music as the horses and the automobiles whirled round and round.

Then there were ever so many amusement booths, each with a crowd standing before it. You won't be surprised to hear that Tonino forgot all about his pottery for a moment, and wanted to climb down from the cart then and there and ride on the merry-go-rounds and visit every booth. But his Mameto told him that it would be much better to sell his pottery first. Then he would have some money to spend at the fair.

Mameto had just caught sight of an inn with a picture of a golden pigeon over the door, called "The Golden Pigeon Inn." The innkeeper was just as friendly as could be. His inn was full, he said, as a lot of strangers had come to Vence for the fair. But he had a tiny room over the stable, with a big double bed. The bed was so big that there was room for hardly any other furniture. But it looked comfortable and clean, and Tonino thought it very nice to be so close to Tintourlet in the stable below.

The innkeeper admired Tintourlet immensely. He said: "You have a very fine donkey. He looks as if he could run fast. Why don't you ride him in the donkey race this afternoon?"

How exciting that would be! Mameto agreed that any donkey would have to run fast to beat Tintourlet. But first, she said, it must be decided how to sell Tonino's pottery.

Then the innkeeper said: "Why don't you let your donkey pull the cart over to the fair grounds? Then you can unharness him and leave the cart with the pottery while you bring him back here. But first take your donkey to the fountain and let him drink. You'll find it on the other side of the Grand Place, just through the gate that leads to the old town. Then I'll give him a good rubdown and a feed of oats, so that he will be fresh for the race this afternoon. You will have the whole morning to sell your pottery at the fair."

SELLING THE POTTERY

So that is exactly what Tonino and Mameto did. Mameto found a corner of the Grand Place that was still unused, and Tonino unharnessed Tintourlet. Then while Mameto unpacked the pottery, he led the donkey through the big gate— and there was the fountain. On the other side of

TONINO TAKES HIS POTTERY TO THE FAIR 139

the fountain was a pottery shop. Outside the shop were great wooden stands with shelves that were filled with beautiful plates and jars and pitchers. Some had pretty pictures painted on them, and some were colored blue or pink or yellow, or all the colors of the rainbow. Already there was quite a crowd of beautifully dressed ladies, carrying bright-colored parasols and admiring the pottery.

Tonino felt a little worried. This pottery was ever so much more beautiful than any that the children in Nouvilo decorated, and the cups and the bowls were ever so much rounder and smoother than any *he* could ever hope to make. But he hoped that perhaps some of the people at the fair would not be so particular.

When Tintourlet had drunk his fill, Tonino led him to the stable at the inn. Then he ran back as fast as he could to where he had left Mameto and the cart.

Mameto had unpacked all the pottery and put it on some newspapers in front of the cart on the ground. As soon as Tonino appeared, she went off by herself to see the fair. What do you think? Hardly had she disappeared when a number of people began to crowd around to see what Tonino was selling. They laughed when they saw his cups and saucers and bowls with funny little animals for handles.

Immediately one lady bought a cup and saucer. Then another lady bought a bowl, and her little girl bought a cup with a little rabbit on it. Behold, Tonino had sold three pieces of pottery! But there were still seventy-three pieces left, and for a long time nobody bought anything. Selling is often a slow business.

Just as Tonino was beginning to feel a tiny bit discouraged, he saw a lady coming toward him. When she saw all Tonino's cups and saucers and bowls spread out on the ground, she stopped.

"What cunning cups and saucers those are," she said. "Where did you get them?"

She was surprised when Tonino told her that he had made them all himself; and that his little sister, Nanou, had painted them.

Then the friendly lady picked up one of the cups. It was the one that had the figure of a cat climbing up the side, instead of a handle. Then she examined the bowl with a donkey sitting on the lid. And what do you think she said?

"I wonder if you would like to sell me all the

141

pottery that you have here," she said. "I have a pottery shop near the fountain, and I am always looking out for something new and different."

Well, I don't have to describe to you what Tonino's feelings were. Think of it! To sell every one of his cups and saucers and bowls! To have the rest of the day free to see the fair and to ride on the merry-go-rounds and to buy presents at the booths!

Just then Mameto came back. She was delighted that the lady who kept the pottery shop had bought all Tonino's pottery, but she was not a bit surprised. Had she not expected it all along?

So she and Tonino and the pottery-shop lady started right away to pack the pottery back in the baskets. Every now and then the lady would notice a cunning little figure, and laugh. Anyone could see that she was as much pleased to buy Tonino's pottery as he was to sell it.

When it was all counted and packed, the pottery-lady told Tonino to hold out his hand while she counted out the money to pay for it. Tonino had never seen so much money at one time in his whole life!

But that was not all. Next the lady asked for Tonino's name and address. She said that she would make a journey to Nouvilo next year and buy six dozen more pieces of his pottery! They were all to be decorated with little animals, like the ones that she had just bought.

Then the lady said that she would send a boy with a cart to carry the two baskets of pottery to her shop. Tonino had told her that his donkey was going to run in the race that very afternoon; so she would not let Tintourlet be disturbed.

Just as the pottery-lady said "Good-by," she asked Mameto where she and Tonino were staying in Vence. As soon as she heard, she said, "I should like to know a great deal more about how Tonino came to make his pottery, and how Nanou paints it. I wonder if you and the little Tonino would have lunch with me at the Golden Pigeon at twelve o'clock?"

Of course Mameto accepted. Imagine the fun of having lunch at one of those little tables in front of the Golden Pigeon instead of eating some bread and cheese on a bench in the Grand Place!

There were ever so many other people having their lunches when Tonino, his grandmother, and the pottery-lady sat down at a little table. That made it all the more interesting.

Tonino had never before eaten so many different things at one meal. First, there were olives and radishes and little sardines. Then they had stuffed tomatoes and eggplant, followed by roast veal and potatoes. For dessert the lady gave an order for ice-cream. Of course, Tonino had never tasted any in his life. He thought it so delicious that he wanted to keep half to give to Nanou when he got back to Nouvilo. He was sorry when he was told that there would be none left when he reached home. But he could not help enjoying the rest of his ice-cream himself, since it was impossible to take it to Nanou.

VISITING THE FAIR

After lunch they sat at the table for a long time. Then the pottery-lady had to go back to her shop, and Tonino and Mameto went off to visit the fair. The donkey race was not to be until four o'clock, when it would be cooler.

Mameto said that as Tonino had earned so much money, he should buy presents to take home with him, and ride on the merry-go-rounds. Of course, that was the thing Tonino wanted most of all to do.

First he rode on a black horse with a red

TONINO TAKES HIS POTTERY TO THE FAIR 145

saddle. It was great fun riding around and around, with the music playing a gay tune that Tonino had never heard before. But the next time he went to the merry-go-round that had automobiles. Here he bought *two* tickets, for Mameto had said that she would like to have a ride in one with him. They chose a pale blue automobile and whirled around and around to the music. Mameto said one ride was enough for her, but Tonino had three more rides on the black horse.

After that he and Mameto went to the booths, where one could buy nice presents. It was hard to choose among so many beautiful things. At last Tonino decided on a doll for Nanou, and I wish that you could have seen it! The doll was dressed like a French flower-girl. She wore a large black hat with feathers, a red and white striped skirt, and a black velvet bodice. Hanging from her shoulders she carried a basket filled with flowers. For his mother, Tonino chose a pretty lace collar to wear with her best yellow dress; for Mameto a box made of polished olive-wood with a bunch of violets painted on the lid, and "Vence" written underneath in golden letters.

Tonino did not forget Tintourlet, either. For him, the little boy bought a straw hat, with holes for his ears to fit through. It was a nice shade-hat and would protect the donkey from the heat of the sun on the journey home. For Minou, the cat, Tonino bought a yellow ribbon to match her yellow eyes; for Lavanda, the goat, a pink ribbon; and for the baby goat, a blue one.

Now all the presents were bought, and Tonino had exactly enough money for three more rides on the merry-go-round. Then it was time to go back to the inn and get Tintourlet, for it was already half-past three.

The race was to be run on one of the country roads just outside of the town. Of course Tintourlet had no saddle, but Tonino had often ridden him without one, and he had never fallen off yet. So he put on the bridle and mounted Tintourlet, and Mameto walked beside him until they reached the starting-place.

THE DONKEY RACE

There were ten donkeys entered for the race; some of them looked very spick and span, with beautiful saddles and stirrups and reins. The ten donkeys were arranged in a row across the road. At a signal, they all started running as hard as they could; that is, all but Tintourlet. He looked about him, and when Tonino clicked his tongue and cried out, "Run, Tintourlet, run!" he began to walk slowly along the road.

Everybody shouted with laughter. I don't know what would have happened if a man had not blown a loud blast on his horn to cheer the race on. It acted like magic on Tintourlet. He put his ears back and dashed forward without even waiting to bray. So fast did he gallop that he hardly seemed to touch the road with his hoofs. In no time he had passed the first donkey and the second one. There were still seven donkeys ahead of him, but Tintourlet put on more speed, and soon there were only two in front, and the crowd was cheering! Still Tintourlet ran faster and faster, and passed the leading donkey just a few yards before he shot under the flag that marked the end of the race.

Tonino couldn't stop him, though he tugged at the bridle with all his might. They had gone nearly half a mile beyond the flag before the donkey would slow up and allow Tonino to turn and walk him back.

The people were still cheering. They said it was the most wonderful donkey race they had ever seen, and that Tintourlet was a racing donkey if ever there was one. Tintourlet had

TONINO TAKES HIS POTTERY TO THE FAIR

won the race at the Big Fair of Vence! The prizes were all to be given that very night at ten o'clock on the Grand Place.

It would take too long to tell you all about the dinner that Tonino and Mameto had at the Golden Pigeon that night. The innkeeper was so proud because the winner of the donkey race was staying under his roof that he invited them all three to dinner. But Tintourlet had his in the stable!

In the evening the fair grounds were very gay. The large open place between the booths was lighted up by tiny electric lights, and at one end there was a band-stand. At eight o'clock the musicians arrived. As soon as they had taken their seats, they tuned up, and the dancing began.

At last ten o'clock struck from the tall church tower. The musicians filed out of the band-stand, and the Mayor of Vence and the members of the committee of festivals took their place.

Can you imagine how Tonino felt? His name was called out, and he climbed up the steps of the band-stand to receive a beautiful new harness for Tintourlet. Of course it was Tintourlet who had really won the prize, though Tonino had done pretty well to stick on his back when he was galloping so fast.

BASIC READERS—BOOK FOUR

Notes and Questions

1. Here is a list of the main things that happened in the story, but they are not in the right order. Put them in the right order.
    - (a) Tonino visits the fair.
    - (b) Tonino sells his pottery.
    - (c) Tonino and Mameto arrive at Vence.
    - (d) Tonino is given the prize.
    - (e) Tonino buys presents for his family.
    - (f) Tintourlet wins the donkey race.
    - (g) Tonino and Mameto put up at the inn.

2. Make a list of the five most important people in this story. You can begin this way: (a) *Tonino, who made the pottery.*

3. Tell in one sentence what this story is about. Begin this way: *This is a story of a French boy who . . .*

4. Why did the lady like Tonino's pottery?
    - (a) Because it was so smooth and round.
    - (b) Because it had such pretty colors.
    - (c) Because it had such cunning little animals on it.

5. What was the funniest part of the story?

6. Be ready to read lines that tell—
    - (a) about Tonino and Mameto at the inn.
    - (b) how Tonino sold the first of his pottery.
    - (c) how the lady bought it all.
    - (d) about the presents Tonino bought.
    - (e) about the donkey race.

If you liked this story, you would enjoy "Bor at Skodra Bazaar," Miller (in *Children of the Mountain Eagle*); *Nanette of the Wooden Shoes*, Brann; and "Mother's Warning to the Wind," Jacobi (in *The Adventures of Andris*).

TING FANG WINS THE SANDAL RACE

Dorothy Rowe

China seems far, far away, and its people seem very strange to us; but Chinese boys and girls are very much like the boys and girls you know. They love their homes and parents, have their lessons to learn, and like to play games. This story tells about a game which may seem queer to you, but the Chinese boys and girls who played it thought it was great fun.

THE BIG RAIN

"Oh, little Ting Fang, it's cold today!" said a Chinese mother as she stood in the door of her poor little house and shivered.

Her son, Ting Fang, stood beside her and looked out into the narrow path between his house and the other houses in Ricksha Man Alley.

"It has rained for two whole days," he said, "and such terrible rain it is! Just like long, silver needles to prick us." Ting Fang shivered, too, and tucked his hands up in his sleeves to keep them warm.

Out in the alley water ran like a river, and the straw roof of the ricksha man's house dripped rain from every corner and all along each side like a very big umbrella. While Mother and Ting Fang were looking out at the wetness and shaking their heads about it, Father came home, pulling his yellow ricksha behind him. He looked like a boatman, walking in water up to his knees; the ricksha looked like a boat sailing along on wheels. It sailed right up to Ting Fang's door; he and his mother stood back while his father pulled the ricksha into the little one-room house and set it in a corner. Then Father took off his straw cape and shook it outside the door, just as a dog shakes himself to get dry.

TING FANG WINS THE SANDAL RACE

Mother started to cook supper in one corner of the room. She had a mud stove in which she burned old straw sandals and bits of grass to cook her supper.

Father said to Ting Fang, "Never since I was a very little boy has there been such a rain as this. Why, along the street the water is up to my knees, and in nearly all the houses it is right on the floor."

"Do you think it will ever stop?" asked Ting Fang, as he listened to the rain patter on the roof and rattle on an old tin pail by the door.

"All the ricksha men say tomorrow will be clear," said Father. "I hope so, for already I have used six pairs of straw sandals and lost them all. And Mother needs them to burn in the stove."

Chinese ricksha men wear straw sandals on their feet. In sunny weather, when the sandals get worn out or broken, the ricksha men take them off and leave them in the streets. Then boys and girls of families who are very poor gather them to take home for fuel. So Ting Fang said, "Too bad, Father, too bad! If the sun shines tomorrow, I will go out and bring in many of the old sandals that the men have lost. When they are dry, Mother will have plenty of fuel to burn."

This is a kind of game that poor children in China play after the rain. They all go out and gather old, wet sandals from the muddy streets and bring them home. They have a race, and the boy or girl who brings home the most sandals wins.

THE RACE STARTS

Early the next morning when the rain had stopped and the sun came out, Mother said to Ting Fang, "You'd better be starting to find sandals for the fire, son. Take the big rope to string the sandals on and bring many home to Mother. Be sure to bring some home by noon, so they will have time to dry before supper, for I have nothing to burn tonight for a fire."

Ting Fang felt very important. He knew his mother was counting on him to bring home enough sandals for the fire. If he did not bring them, there would be no hot supper for Father when he came home from work.

Rolling up his trousers above his knees so that they would not be spattered with mud, Ting Fang tied his long coat around his waist. Then, with the long rope in his hand, he started out. Most of the rickshas travel on the Big Horse Road; so Ting Fang went to that road first. There were many other children there, already sandal-hunting, and they called, "Hey, Ting Fang of Ricksha Man Alley! Come and race with us. We are just starting. Have you a long rope?"

"I certainly have," answered Ting Fang. "Are you going to get home by twelve o'clock? I have to be home then so that I can have some sandals dried by supper-time."

"Yes," said the leader of the race, "we will be home by twelve." And off the children started, excited and happy.

Ting Fang found the first sandal. It was lying by the road and was a very dirty, wet piece of straw. Ting Fang shouted when he found it, and the children called, "Good luck, Ting Fang, good luck!" Ting Fang picked up the sandal, put his rope through the hole in the heel, and started off again, pulling the sandal along behind him. Pulling one sandal is easy, but pulling twenty or thirty is hard work.

When the children had been hunting for an hour, Ting Fang was ahead. He had twenty-five sandals, and the little girl who came next had only sixteen. The whole crowd of boys and girls walked a long way on the Big Horse Road, picking up every sandal they could find. Next they turned down North Gate Street, where the stores pushed right to the very edge, and where there were always many people and rickshas.

Once the little girl, who now was only six sandals behind Ting Fang, saw four sandals bunched together right by the edge of a deep ditch. She went scrambling to get them and almost fell into the ditch. When she called out, Ting Fang ran to help her. He pulled her out and laughed at her. "Did you want to take a bath?" he said. He helped the little girl back to the road again and then reached into the ditch and got the sandals for her. "You take them," the little girl said.

"You really got them, Ting Fang." But he said, "No, you saw them first; so you keep them." The little girl was now only two behind Ting Fang.

There is a place in that city where the road runs between two deep ponds. It is a narrow road, with the water coming right up to the edge on each side. Ting Fang knew it was a dangerous road, but he knew that many sandals could be found there. So he told the other children that he was going to the Road Between Ponds and that he would meet them at twelve o'clock.

TING FANG LOSES HIS SANDALS

Ting Fang was very happy as he walked along. All the way he sang a song and pulled his heavy load of sandals. At the Road Between Ponds the mud was slippery, and the deep water was very close. In just a little while Ting Fang found six sandals and strung them on his rope. The string of sandals was now very heavy, and the rope seemed longer than before.

Soon the little boy saw another sandal right by the edge of the pond. As he reached for it, he suddenly slipped and almost fell into the deep water. He was so frightened that he dropped his rope and used both hands to climb back to the road again. Then he stood up and looked for his rope. It was not there! Ting Fang could hardly believe it, but it was true. His rope, with the heavy sandals, had slid off the edge of the road into the water, and the sandals were lost forever!

Ting Fang did not know what to do. He would not win the race, of course, but worse than that, he would have no sandals to take home, and Mother could not cook without them. There would not be any hot supper for Father when he came home from work. Ting Fang tried not to cry as he walked along to Big Horse Road again. The children ran to meet him with their long ropes of sandals dragging behind them.

"How many did you get, Ting Fang?" they cried, and then stopped in surprise when they saw that he had no rope in his hand.

"Where are your sandals?" one asked.

"I have lost them," said Ting Fang, struggling hard to keep back his tears.

"Oh, Ting Fang," said the little girl whom he had helped out of the ditch earlier that morning, "where did you lose them?"

"The rope slipped off the Road Between Ponds, and all my sandals are down at the bottom of the pond. Mother will have no fire tonight. You

TING FANG WINS THE SANDAL RACE

won after all," Ting Fang ended, trying to smile at the little girl who had been second in the race.

"But you helped me," she cried. "Wait here a moment—perhaps I can help you now."

THE SANDALS ARE SAVED

Before Ting Fang or the other children had time to ask her what she meant, the little girl had rushed off down the Big Horse Road. The children sat down, wondering how poor Ting Fang could ever get his sandals back.

In a few moments they saw the little girl coming back, and with her was a tall young man.

"Who is he? What is he going to do?" the children whispered; but the little girl only laughed happily, and the young man said, "Wait and see."

Then Ting Fang led the way to the Road Between Ponds. When they came to the narrow street, the tall young man told the children to wait while he and Ting Fang crept carefully along the narrow strip of land between the ponds.

"Now show me where the rope slid in," the children heard the young man say to Ting Fang.

Ting Fang pointed to the spot. There was still the mark of the rope on the muddy road like the mark of a water snake.

And then before the children could guess what was happening, the young man had dived into the pond. In a moment he was up again, tossing his hair from his eyes and smiling at the little girl, who was saying: "Did you find them?"

"The pond is so muddy that I cannot see the bottom," said the young man; "and so I must feel for the sandals."

Then he ducked his head under again and the children saw his feet go in last like the flopping tail of a great fish. He was under for a long time. But suddenly—up he came, and in his hand was the rope with the wet sandals dangling from it. Ting Fang helped to pull in the rope himself and counted the sandals as they came out of the water. He had lost only a few, and even without those he still had more sandals than anyone else.

"Thank you, thank you!" Ting Fang said to the hero who had saved his sandals. "Now my mother can cook our supper tonight. But how did you learn to dive so well?" he asked.

The tall young man smiled. "I am a sailor," he answered. "On my ship there is a workman who used to earn his living by diving for pearls, and he has taught me how to dive. This man and I amuse ourselves by dropping things overboard and then bringing them back to the ship."

"How did you know about this wonderful diver?" Ting Fang asked the little girl.

"I ought to know. He is my big brother, and he just came home for a few days' rest," said the little girl proudly. "Last night he told us all about the diving."

The sandal race was over. Ting Fang was happy because he had so many sandals to take home to his mother. And all the little children on Big Horse Road talked for a long time about the tall young man who could swim like a fish and had been taught by a pearl diver to bring things up from the bottom of the sea.

NOTES AND QUESTIONS

1. To see whether you understand this story, answer these questions:
    (a) What did the Chinese children collect?
    (b) Why were these things thrown away?
    (c) Why did the children collect them?
    (d) How did they carry them?

2. Name five interesting things you learned about China. Begin this way: (a) *Straw is used for roofs.* Perhaps the pictures will help you find things.

3. Do you think other ricksha men lived on Ting Fang's street? Why?

4. Which was the one thing that made it possible for Ting Fang to bring home a long string of sandals?
    (a) He hunted hard.
    (b) He was kind to the little girl.
    (c) He went to the dangerous Road Between Ponds.

5. Make up a name, or title, for each picture in the story. You can call the first one "Ting Fang's father comes home in the big rain." Now name the others.

Dorothy Rowe, who wrote this story, lived in China for many years. She loved the Chinese boys and girls, and wrote many true stories about them. You would enjoy reading "Seiji and the Pearls," in her book, *The Begging Deer;* and "Ting Ping and the Very Black Kitty," in *The Rabbit Lantern,* another of her books. You would also like "A Chinese Secret," by Carolyn Mabry (in *Child Life,* Sept., 1929).

THE LITTLE TOY LAND OF THE DUTCH

Away, 'way off 'cross the seas and such
Lies the little flat land of the Dutch, Dutch, Dutch,

Where the green toy meadows stretch off to the sea,
With a little canal where a fence ought to be!

Where the windmill's arms go round, round, round,
And sing to the cows with a creaky sound.

Where storks live up in the chimney-top,
And wooden shoes pound, plop, plop, plop!

Where little toy houses stand in a row,
And dog carts clattering past them go!

Where milk-cans shine in the shiniest way,
And the housemaids scrub, scrub, scrub all day.

Where dikes keep out the raging sea,
And shut in the land as cozy as can be.

Oh, that little toy land, I like it much,
That prim little, trim little, land of the Dutch.

A BACKWARD LOOK

JUST think of the long journey you have taken! In only a few days you have visited five different countries. Can you name them? Perhaps you can find each of these countries on your geography maps or on the wall map in your room. Which of the countries are close together?

Did you meet any boys and girls on your travels that were like boys and girls you know at home? It would be fun to choose the country you would most like to visit, and collect pictures of that country for a scrapbook or for the bulletin board.

Was there one of these stories that you liked best? Which one was it, and why? Have you ever read any other stories of far-away lands? Your classmates and your teacher would be glad to know of stories you have read and liked.

There are many people who like to read travel books better than any other kind. If you go to the library, you will find hundreds of books about far-away lands. Almost every nook and corner of the earth from the North Pole to the South Pole, and from East to West, has been written about. People have always liked to travel, and when they cannot travel, they read books about the lands they would like to visit.

Would you like to read more stories about far-away lands? On page 370 you will find the names of some books you would enjoy reading.

PART · IV

STORIES EVERYONE SHOULD KNOW

CLIMBING

High up in the apple tree climbing I go,
With the sky above me, the earth below.
Each branch is the step of a wonderful stair
Which leads to the town I see shining up there.

Climbing, climbing, higher and higher,
The branches blow and I see a spire,
The gleam of a turret, the glint of a dome,
All sparkling and bright, like white sea-foam.

Today to the end of the marvelous stair,
Where those glittering pinnacles flash in the air!
Climbing, climbing, higher I go,
With the sky close above me, the earth far below.

—*Amy Lowell*

EVERYONE LIKES A GOOD STORY

EVEN before you could read, you used to ask your father and mother to tell you stories. Everyone likes a good story. All over our land there are thousands of libraries, and every year millions of people are reading stories—in books, in magazines, and in newspapers.

Now, of course, not everyone likes the same kind of story. You like some better than others. But there are stories that everyone seems to enjoy; the years go by, the stories get older, and yet people go on reading them and enjoying them.

Now your Book Comrade will tell you three stories that millions of people have enjoyed. Two of them are old, written long before you or your parents were born. But people still read them, and probably will do so for many long years to come. No one knows who first made them up. One of them is given here as it was written down by a great American storyteller, another as it was retold by an English writer of today. You could find thousands of boys and girls in lands across the sea who know these stories. The third story is not so old, but people have loved it for many years, and you will love it, too.

After you have read these stories, perhaps you can find others that you will enjoy very much. Then you will be able to tell other people about these stories.

THE MIRACULOUS PITCHER
Nathaniel Hawthorne

Nathaniel Hawthorne was one of America's greatest story-tellers. In some of his stories he told of famous wonder-working people who were supposed to live long years ago. They were called gods, and they ruled over the people who lived on earth. The father of all the gods was Zeus. The thunder was his voice, and lightning was his weapon. Quicksilver was the messenger of the gods. In the story you will now read, Hawthorne tells how Zeus and Quicksilver came down to earth, and taught some people a very valuable lesson.

BAUCIS AND PHILEMON

One evening, in times long ago, old Philemon and his wife, Baucis, sat at their cottage door, enjoying the beautiful sunset. They had already eaten their supper, and intended to spend a quiet hour or two before bedtime.

So they talked together about their garden and their cow and their bees. But the rude shouts of children and the fierce barking of dogs in the village near at hand grew louder and louder, until at last it was hardly possible for Baucis and Philemon to hear each other speak.

"Ah, wife," cried Philemon, "I fear some poor traveler is seeking hospitality among our neighbors and, instead of giving him food and lodging they have set their dogs at him."

"Well!" answered old Baucis, "I do wish our neighbors felt a little more kindness for their fellow-creatures. Only think of bringing up their children in this naughty way, and patting them on the head when they fling stones at strangers!"

"Those children will never come to any good," said Philemon, shaking his white head. "To tell you the truth, wife, I should not wonder if some terrible thing were to happen to all the people in the village if they do not learn to behave themselves. But as for you and me, so long as we have a crust of bread, let us be ready to give half to any poor homeless stranger that may come along and need it."

"That's right, husband!" said Baucis. "So we will!"

These old folks, you must know, were quite poor, and had to work pretty hard for a living. Their food was usually bread, milk, and vegetables, with sometimes honey from their beehive.

But they were two of the kindest old people in the world. They would cheerfully have gone without their dinners any day, rather than refuse a slice of their brown loaf, a cup of new milk, and

THE MIRACULOUS PITCHER

a spoonful of honey to the weary traveler who might stop at their door.

Their cottage stood a short distance from the village, which lay in a valley. This valley, when the world was new, had probably been the bed of a lake. There, fishes had glided to and fro in the depths, and the water-weeds had grown along the shore. But it was now a fertile spot of fields and meadows.

Never was there a prettier or more fruitful valley. The very sight of the beautiful fields and orchards with their rich crops should have made the people kind and gentle, and ready to do good to their fellow-men. But, we are sorry to say, the men and women of this lovely valley were very selfish and hardhearted, and had no pity for the poor.

You will hardly believe what I am going to tell you. These naughty people used to clap their hands when they saw the little boys and girls run after some poor stranger, shouting at his heels and pelting him with stones. They kept large and fierce dogs, and whenever a stranger showed himself in the village street, this pack of ugly curs scampered to meet him, barking and snarling.

THE TWO TRAVELERS

So now you can understand why old Philemon spoke so sorrowfully when he heard the shouts of the children and the barking of the dogs.

"I never heard the dogs so loud!" said the good old man.

"Nor the children so rude!" answered his wife.

They sat shaking their heads one to another, while the noise came nearer and nearer, until they saw two travelers approaching on foot. Close behind them came the fierce dogs, snarling at their very heels. A little farther off ran a crowd

THE MIRACULOUS PITCHER 171

of children, who flung stones at the two strangers with all their might.

Both of the travelers were very poorly clad, and looked as if they might not have money enough in their pockets to pay for a night's lodging.

"Come, wife," said Philemon to Baucis, "let us go and meet these poor people. No doubt they feel almost too heavy-hearted to climb the hill."

"Go you and meet them," answered Baucis, "while I make haste within doors and see whether we can get them anything for supper."

And so she hastened to the cottage. Philemon went forward, saying in the heartiest tone: "Welcome, strangers! Welcome!"

"Thank you!" replied the younger of the two. "This is quite another greeting than the one we have met with in the village. Those children— the little rascals!—have spattered us from head to foot with their mud-balls; and one of the curs has torn my cloak, which was ragged enough already."

He was dressed in rather an odd way, with a sort of cap on his head, the brim of which stuck out over both ears. Though it was summer-time, he wore a cloak. Philemon saw, too, that he had on a strange-looking pair of shoes.

THE MARVELOUS STAFF

One thing certainly seemed queer. The traveler was so wonderfully light and active that it appeared as if his feet sometimes rose from the ground of their own accord.

"I used to be light-footed in my youth," said Philemon to the traveler. "But I always found my feet grow heavier toward night-fall."

"There is nothing like a good staff to help one along," answered the stranger; "and I happen to have an excellent one, as you see."

This staff, in fact, was the oddest-looking staff that Philemon had ever seen. It was made of olive-wood, and had something like a pair of wings near the top. Two snakes carved in the wood were twining themselves about the staff. Old Philemon almost thought them alive, and that he could see them wriggling and twisting.

"A curious piece of work, sure enough!" said he. "A staff with wings! It would be an excellent kind of stick for a little boy to ride astride of!"

By this time Philemon and his two guests had reached the cottage door.

"Friends," said the old man, "sit down and rest yourselves here on this bench. My good wife, Baucis, has gone to see what you can have for supper. We are poor folks; but you shall be welcome to whatever we have in the cupboard."

The younger stranger threw himself carelessly on the bench, letting his staff fall as he did so. And here happened something rather marvelous. The staff seemed to get up from the ground! Spreading its little pair of wings, it half hopped, half flew, and leaned itself against the wall of the cottage. There it stood quite still, except that the snakes continued to wriggle.

Before Philemon could ask any questions, the elder stranger inquired in a deep voice, "Was there not, in very old times, a lake covering the spot where now stands yonder village?"

"Not in my day, friend," answered Philemon, "and yet I am an old man, as you see. There were always the fields and meadows, just as now, and doubtless it will be the same when old Philemon shall be gone and forgotten."

"That is more than can be safely told," said the stranger; and there was something very stern in his deep voice. He shook his head, too, so that his dark and heavy curls were shaken with the movement. "Since the people of the village are so unkind, it would be better if the lake should ripple over their dwellings again!"

The traveler looked so stern that Philemon was almost frightened. But, in a moment, his face became so kindly that the old man quite forgot his terror. Still, he could not help feeling that this elder traveler was not an ordinary person, although he happened to be dressed so humbly.

While Baucis was getting the supper, the travelers both began to talk with Philemon. The younger was so witty that the good old man often burst out laughing, and called him the merriest fellow he had seen for many a day.

"Pray, my young friend," said he, "what may I call your name?"

"Why, I am very nimble, as you see," answered the traveler. "So, if you call me Quicksilver, the name will fit well."

"Quicksilver? Quicksilver?" said Philemon, looking in the traveler's face to see if he were making fun of him. "It is a very odd name. And your companion there? Has he as strange a one?"

"You must ask the thunder to tell it to you," replied Quicksilver. "No other voice is loud enough."

Baucis had now got supper ready, and, coming to the door, began to make apologies for the poor food which she had made ready for her guests.

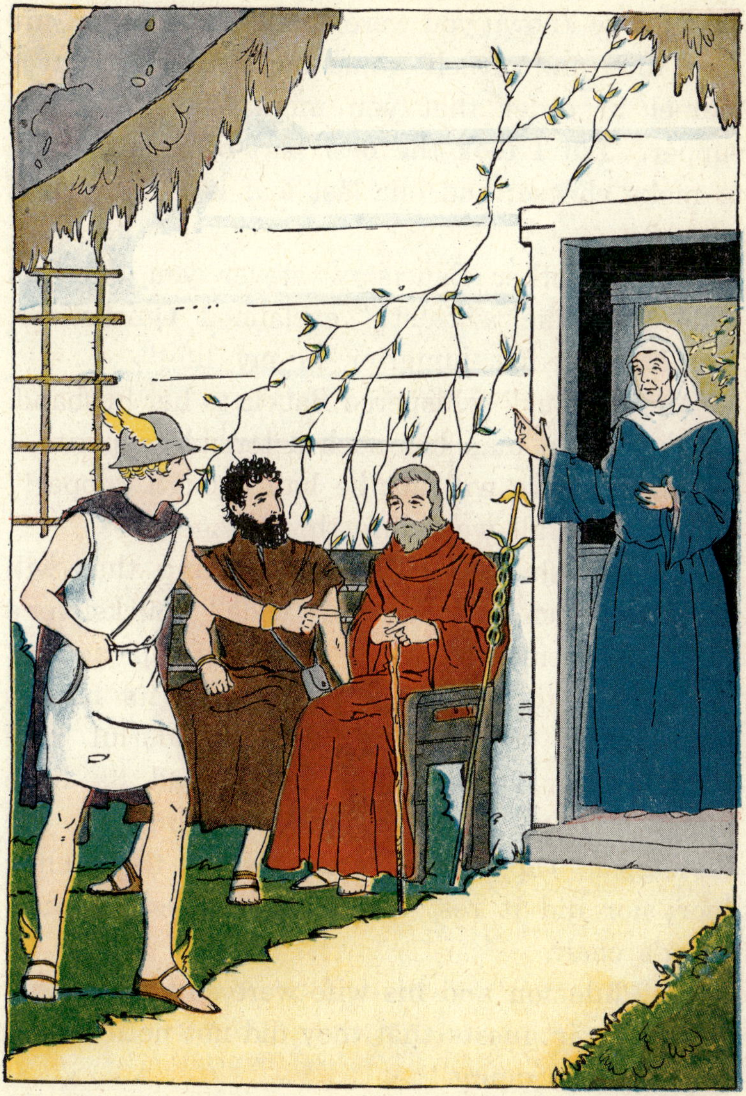

"Had we known you were coming," said she, "my good man and myself would have gone without a morsel in order that you might have a better supper. But I took the best part of today's milk to make cheese; and our last loaf is already half eaten."

"Why, Mother Baucis, whatever you offer us will seem like a feast!" exclaimed Quicksilver, "for I never felt hungrier in my life!"

"Mercy on us!" whispered Baucis to her husband. "If the young man has such a terrible appetite, I am afraid there will not be half enough supper!"

Then they all went into the cottage.

And now shall I tell you something that will make you open your eyes very wide? Quicksilver's staff, you remember, had set itself up against the wall of the cottage. Well, when its master entered the door, leaving this wonderful staff behind, what should it do but spread its little wings and go hopping and fluttering up the doorsteps! Tap, tap, went the staff on the kitchen floor; nor did it rest until it stood beside Quicksilver's chair.

Old Philemon and his wife were so busy taking care of their guests that they did not notice what the staff was doing.

THE WONDERFUL SUPPER

As Baucis had said, there was but a scanty supper for two hungry travelers. In the middle of the table was part of a brown loaf, with a piece of cheese on one side of it, and a dish of honeycomb on the other. A pitcher nearly full of milk stood at a corner of the table; and when Baucis had filled two bowls and set them before the strangers, only a little milk remained at the bottom of the pitcher.

Poor Baucis kept wishing that she might starve for a week to come, if it were possible by so doing to provide these hungry folks with a more plentiful supper. And since the supper was so small, she could not help wishing that their appetites had not been quite so large. Why, at their very first sitting down the travelers both drank off all the milk in their two bowls!

"A little more milk, kind Mother Baucis, if you please," said Quicksilver. "The day has been hot, and I am very thirsty."

"Now, my dear people," answered Baucis, "I am so sorry and ashamed! But the truth is, there is hardly a drop more milk in the pitcher."

"Why, it seems to me," cried Quicksilver, starting up from the table and taking the pitcher by the handle, "it really seems to me that there is more milk in the pitcher."

So saying, he filled not only his own bowl but his companion's also from the pitcher that was supposed to be almost empty. The good woman could scarcely believe her eyes. She had certainly poured out nearly all the milk; and she had peeped in afterwards and seen the bottom of the pitcher as she set it down on the table.

"But I am old," thought Baucis to herself, "and apt to be forgetful. I suppose I must have made a mistake."

"What excellent milk!" said Quicksilver, after drinking the second bowl. "Excuse me, my kind hostess, but I must really ask you for a little more."

Now Baucis had seen as plainly as she could see anything, that Quicksilver had turned the pitcher upside down and had poured out every drop of milk in filling the last bowl. Of course, there could not possibly be any left.

She lifted the pitcher as if pouring milk into Quicksilver's bowl, but without any idea that any milk would stream forth. What was her surprise, when the bowl was filled to the brim and overflowed upon the table! The two snakes that were twisted about Quicksilver's staff stretched out

THE MIRACULOUS PITCHER

their heads and began to lap up the spilled milk.

"And now a slice of your brown loaf, Mother Baucis," said Quicksilver, "and a little of that honey!"

Baucis cut him a slice, and although the loaf, when she and her husband ate of it, had been rather dry and crusty, it was now as light and moist as if but a few hours out of the oven. Tasting a crumb which had fallen on the table, she found it more delicious than bread ever was before, and could hardly believe that it was a loaf of her own baking.

But, oh, the honey! Its color was that of the purest gold; and it had the odor of a thousand flowers. Never was such honey tasted, seen, or smelled.

Although good Mother Baucis was a simple old dame, she could not help thinking that there was something rather uncommon in all that had been going on. So, after helping the guests to bread and honey, she sat down by Philemon, and told him in a whisper what she had seen.

"Did you ever hear the like?" she asked.

"No, I never did," answered Philemon with a smile. "And I rather think, my dear old wife, that you have been walking about in a sort of dream. There happened to be a little more in the pitcher than you thought—that is all."

"Ah, husband," said Baucis, "say what you will, these are very uncommon people."

"Well, well," replied Philemon, still smiling, "perhaps they are. They certainly do look as if they had seen better days."

"Another bowl of this delicious milk, if you please," said Quicksilver, "and I shall then have supped better than a prince."

This time old Philemon took up the pitcher, for he was curious to see whether there was any

THE MIRACULOUS PITCHER

truth in what Baucis had whispered to him. On taking up the pitcher, he slyly peeped into it; he was sure that it did not contain a single drop. But all at once he saw a little white fountain, which gushed up from the bottom of the pitcher and filled it to the brim with foaming and delicious milk.

"Who are you, wonder-working strangers?" cried he, even more surprised than his wife had been.

"Your guests, my good Philemon, and your friends," replied the elder traveler, in his deep voice. "Give me, also, a cup of the milk, and may your pitcher never be empty."

THE PUNISHMENT OF THE VILLAGERS

The supper being now over, the strangers asked to be shown to their place of rest; and when Philemon drew Quicksilver aside, and inquired how under the sun a fountain of milk could have got into an old earthen pitcher, he pointed to his staff.

"I can't tell what to make of my staff," said Quicksilver. "It is always playing such odd tricks as this; sometimes getting me a supper, and quite as often stealing it away."

When alone, the good old couple spent some

time in conversation about the events of the evening, and then lay down on the floor and fell fast asleep. They had given up their sleeping-room to the guests and had no other bed for themselves except these planks.

The old man and his wife were stirring early in the morning, and the strangers arose with the sun and made ready to depart.

Philemon asked them to remain until Baucis could milk the cow and find them a few eggs for breakfast. The guests, however, seemed to think it better to travel a good part of their journey before the heat of the day should come on. They therefore set out, but asked Philemon and Baucis to walk with them a short distance, and show them the road which they were to take.

So they all four started from the cottage, chatting together like old friends. "Ah, me!" exclaimed Philemon, when they had walked a little way from the door, "if our neighbors only knew what a blessed thing it is to show hospitality to strangers, they would tie up all their dogs and never allow their children to fling another stone."

"It is a sin and shame for them to behave so— that it is!" cried good old Baucis. "And I mean to tell some of them what naughty people they are!"

"I fear," remarked Quicksilver, slyly smiling, "that you will find none of them at home. And by-the-by, my dear old people, where is the village that you talk about? On which side of us does it lie? I do not see it."

Philemon and his wife turned toward the valley, where at sunset only the day before they had seen the meadows, the houses, the gardens, the trees, and the wide street, with children playing in it. But what was their surprise! There was no longer any village! Even the fertile valley had gone. In its place they saw the broad blue surface of a lake, which filled the great basin of the valley from brim to brim. The village had been there yesterday, and now was gone.

"Alas!" cried these kind-hearted old people, "what has become of our poor neighbors?"

"They live no longer as men and women," said the elder traveler in his deep voice. "There was neither use nor beauty in such a life as theirs, for they never sweetened the sorrow of others."

"Those foolish people," said Quicksilver, "are all changed to fishes. So, kind Mother Baucis, whenever you or your husband has an appetite for a dish of broiled trout, you can throw in a line and pull out half a dozen of your old neighbors."

"Ah," cried Baucis, shuddering, "I would not for the world put one of them on the gridiron!"

"No," added Philemon, making a wry face; "we could never relish them!"

THE REWARD OF BAUCIS AND PHILEMON

"As for you, good Philemon," said the elder traveler—"and you, kind Baucis, ask whatever favor you have most at heart, and it is granted."

Philemon and Baucis looked at one another, and then replied, "Let us live together while we live, and leave the world at the same instant when we die! For we have always loved one another!"

"Be it so," replied the stranger. "Now look toward your cottage!"

They did so. But what was their surprise to see a tall palace of white marble on the spot where their humble home had so lately stood!

"There is your home," said the stranger, smiling on them both. "Show hospitality in the palace as freely as in the poor cottage to which you welcomed us last evening."

The old folks fell on their knees to thank him, but behold! neither he nor Quicksilver was there.

So Philemon and Baucis lived in the marble palace, and spent their time in making everybody comfortable who happened to pass that way. The milk-pitcher, I must not forget to say, was never empty.

Whenever an honest and good-humored guest took a drink from this pitcher, he found it the sweetest fluid that ever ran down his throat. But if anyone cross and disagreeable happened to sip, he was pretty certain to twist his face into a hard knot and call it a pitcher of sour milk!

Thus the old couple lived in their palace a great, great while, and grew older and older, and very old indeed. But at last there came a morning when Philemon and Baucis did not come to invite the guests to breakfast.

The guests searched everywhere, all to no purpose. But they saw in front of the entrance to the palace two trees which nobody could remember having seen before. Yet there they stood, with their roots fastened deep into the soil. One was an oak, and the other a linden tree. Their boughs embraced one another, so that each tree seemed to live in the other tree's bosom.

While the guests were wondering how these trees could have come to be so tall in a single night, a breeze sprang up and set their boughs astir. And then there was a deep murmur in the air, as if the two trees were speaking.

"I am old Philemon!" murmured the oak.

"I am old Baucis!" murmured the linden tree.

THE MIRACULOUS PITCHER

It was plain enough that the good old couple were now to spend a quiet hundred years or so, Philemon as an oak, and Baucis as a linden tree. And oh, what a kindly shade did they fling around them! Whenever anyone paused beneath, he heard a pleasant whisper of the leaves:

"Welcome, welcome, dear traveler, welcome!"

And someone that knew what would have pleased Baucis and Philemon best, built a seat all around their trunks, where for long afterwards the weary, the hungry, and the thirsty used to rest and drink milk from the miraculous pitcher.

And I wish, for all our sakes, that we had the pitcher here now!

NOTES AND QUESTIONS

1. What lesson is Nathaniel Hawthorne trying to teach?
   (a) That bad people are always punished.
   (b) That we should love trees.
   (c) That we should be kind-hearted.

2. Tell four very surprising things in this story. Perhaps you can find more than four.

3. In the picture on page 170, find something strange-looking about Quicksilver.

4. What was it that helped Quicksilver work magic?

5. Why did Quicksilver say that only the thunder would be loud enough to speak his companion's name? You may have to read again the note at the beginning of the story to answer this.

6. Why did the people in the village have every reason to be kind and honest?

7. What reward did Baucis and Philemon choose?

8. How were they rewarded: (a) while they lived, (b) afterwards?

9. Did the travelers really need to have Baucis and Philemon show them the way, or did they have some other reason for asking them to go with them?

10. For each word in the first column below, there is a word or phrase in the second column that means about the same thing. Write the pairs of words together.

(a) heavy-hearted	enjoy
(b) twining	small piece
(c) nimble	sorrowful
(d) wry	stay
(e) morsel	twisting around
(f) remain	quick
(g) hospitality	food and shelter
(h) relish	unpleasant

11. On pages 168 and 173 there are lines that make you think some punishment may come to the people of the village. Find these lines and be ready to read them.

12. In the first two pages of the story, find lines that best tell what kind of people Philemon and Baucis were.

13. On page 182 Philemon says something about his neighbors that shows he was truly a kind-hearted man. Find the lines and be ready to read them.

You would enjoy reading "The Pomegranate Seeds," Hawthorne, and "Salt," Ransome (in *Child-Library Readers, Book Four*); and "Baucis and Philemon," Wickes (in *A Child's Book of Holiday Plays*).

RUMPLESTILTSKIN

Walter de la Mare

Here is an old fairy story that thousands of people in many parts of the world have read. It was first written by Jacob and William Grimm, two famous German storytellers, about one hundred years ago. But long before they wrote it down on paper, people told it to one another. No one knows who first made it up.

THE MILLER'S BOAST

Once upon a time there was a poor miller who had a beautiful daughter. He loved her dearly, and was so proud of her that he could never keep from boasting of her beauty. One morning a stranger came to the mill with a sack of corn to be ground, and he saw the miller's daughter standing by the clattering mill-wheel in the sunshine.

He looked at her and said he wished that he had a daughter as beautiful as she. The miller rubbed his mealy hands together and looked at her, too; and, seeing the sunbeams shining in her hair, answered, almost without thinking:

"Yes! She's a lass in a thousand. She can spin straw into gold."

Now this saying was quickly spread around, and

at last reached the ears of the king. He at once sent for the miller and bade him bring his daughter with him.

"It has been told me," said the king, "that this maid can spin straw into gold. So she shall. But if she fails, then look to it! You shall hang from your own mill."

The miller was so shaken with fear of the king that his tongue stuck in his throat, and he could make no answer.

THE DWARF APPEARS

Then the king led the miller's daughter into a stable, in which were two or three bundles of straw. He looked at the miller's daughter and smiled. "There," said he, "you have straw enough. Spin that into gold before morning." Having said this, with his own hand he locked the door, and left her to herself.

She looked at the spinning-wheel, and she looked at the straw; and at the thought of what would happen on the morrow, she cried, "O father! father!" and burst into tears. As she sat there weeping, there was a rustling, and again a rustling. Then out from under the straw came a little midget of a man, with a peaked hat on his head, long thin legs, a red nose, and a rusty-colored beard that swept down even below his belt.

"What's all this crying about?" he asked angrily. "I can't get a minute's rest from it."

The miller's daughter was so surprised at the sight of him that she stopped crying and told him all.

He laughed at her. "Spin straw into gold! Why, that's no trouble. What will you give me if I spin it for you?"

The miller's daughter gazed at the dwarf through her tears. She had never before seen so odd and ugly-looking a little man. But he looked back at her out of his needle-sharp eyes with such cunning that she half believed that he could do what he said.

She promised to give him her coral necklace. On hearing that, he snapped his fingers in the air, took off his hat, sat down on a three-legged milking stool in front of the spinning-wheel, and began to spin.

Whir, whirr, whirrr! The straw seemed to fly through the air, as if caught up in a wind. And in a moment, behold! All the straw was gold thread, heaped neatly together, and the stable was swept empty.

The little long-nosed man got down from his stool as fresh as a daisy. Then he put the coral necklace into the little bag which he carried, and off he went.

When next morning the king saw the thread, all of pure gold, he was mightily pleased. But his greed for more gold grew with every glance at the golden heap.

"Well and fair," said he, "well and fair. You shall try again."

THE DWARF COMES AGAIN

Then once more he shut up the miller's daughter in a stable, at least half of which was filled with straw. "Spin that into gold," he said, "and you shall have praise indeed. If you fail me—but why think of that!"

For as the king looked at the miller's daughter, he saw how beautiful she was, and in his heart he pitied her a little, though he said nothing. He turned on his heel, went out of the stable, locked the door, and left her to herself.

The miller's daughter was greatly troubled. Yesterday's straw was only a handful compared with what she now had to spin. She looked at the wheel, she looked at the straw, and cried to herself: "Oh, if only that little long-nosed man were here again!"

Sadly she sat down at the wheel and tried to spin. But spin she couldn't, and the straw in her fingers remained only straw. "No hope! no hope! no hope!" she thought. But while these words were still in her mind, the dwarf appeared again out of the straw.

"Ah-ha!" said he. "What's wrong now?" She told him.

"And what will you give me *this* time, if I

spin for you?" he said. She promised him the silver ring on her finger.

Down he sat, flung his beard over his shoulder, snapped his fingers, and began to spin.

Whir, whirr, whirrr, went the spinning-wheel. The straw seemed to slide like melted metal through the air. Smaller and smaller grew the heap of straw; and before dawn it was all gold.

The king could hardly believe his eyes, but even yet his greedy mind was not satisfied. So he smiled at the miller's daughter and said to her: "Well and fair! Well and fair, indeed! Only one more night's work, my dear, and your spinning is over."

RUMPLESTILTSKIN 195

A STRANGE BARGAIN

Then he took her into a barn which was heaped up almost to its roof with yellow straw.

"Spin that into gold for me," he said, "and tomorrow you shall be queen."

With a glance over his shoulder, he went out of the barn, locked the door, and left her to herself.

The miller's daughter sat down. She looked at the spinning-wheel. She looked at the great heap of straw. "Ah," she said, "to spin that into gold would take a hundred little long-nosed men."

"What, what, what!" cried a voice, and in an instant little Master Long-Nose appeared once more, his eyes like green beads and his cheeks like red crab-apples. But this night the miller's daughter had nothing left to offer him for wages. The dwarf looked at her for a moment, and then he said:

"In the seed is the leaf and the bud and the rose,
But what's in the future, why, nobody knows.

"See here, pretty maid; promise me your first child if you ever have one, and queen you shall be tomorrow."

The miller's daughter could only smile at this,

not believing at all that such a thing could ever be; and she promised him. Then the dwarf snapped his fingers in the air, spun around nine times on his toe, and at once sat down to the wheel. *Whirr, whirrr, whirrrr,* went the wheel like the buzzing of bees in summer. *Whirr—whirrr—whirrrr—whirrrrr—whirrrrrr—*and a few minutes before the sun rose next morning the barn was swept clean, and the straw was all gold. Then off the dwarf went.

The king kept his word and made the miller's daughter his queen. And, although his queen had been only a miller's daughter, few queens have been as beautiful; and fewer still have brought their husbands so much gold.

HOW THE NAME WAS FOUND OUT

Some years later the queen sat playing with her baby daughter one May morning in the orchard of the king's palace. As she played, sometimes she laughed, and sometimes she sang, for she was happy. But all in a moment her happiness was changed to fear, for—as if he had sprung straight out of the trunk of a crooked old apple tree near by—there stood the dwarf.

The dwarf looked at the queen, and looked at

RUMPLESTILTSKIN

her baby. "Ah-ha! A pretty thing!" he said. "And mine!"

Now the queen had been happy for so long that she had almost forgotten the promise she had made in her trouble. She pleaded with the dwarf. She agreed to give him anything else he wished, if only he would free her from her promise.

"Nay, nay!" said he at last, "a princess is a princess, and a promise is a promise. Still, I'll make another bargain with you. You shall have three days, and nine guesses. If at the end of the third day and at the ninth guess, you cannot tell me my name, then the child shall be mine." And off he went.

The queen thought and thought. She thought all night long, without a single wink of sleep. Hundreds of names came into her mind. In the morning she went sadly out alone into the orchard, and at the very instant of noon the dwarf popped out again from behind the old apple tree.

"Ah-ha!" said he. "And what's my name, ma'am?"

The queen guessed. First she said, "Abracadabra." The dwarf shook his head. Next she said, "Catalawampus." The dwarf shook his head. Her third guess was just as the word came into her head, "Nickerruckerubblegrubb!"

The dwarf broke into a wild peal of laughter, squeaked, "Try again," and off he went.

All that night the queen lay wide awake, a lighted candle beside her bed. Three times she crept out and stooped over the cradle where her baby lay asleep. But each time she returned to her bed she thought of all the names she had ever heard of when she lived with her father at the mill. And at noon next day once more the dwarf appeared.

"Ah-ha!" said he. "Three and three make six, ma'am!"

First the queen guessed, "Sheepshanks." Next she guessed, "Littlebody." At last she guessed, "Long-Nose."

The dwarf danced about, clapped his hands, shouted, "Try again!" and off he went.

The queen hastened back at once to the palace and sent for a messenger who was sharp of hearing and as keen of eye as a hawk. She told him in secret what the little dwarf looked like, with his thin legs, his red nose, his long, rusty beard, and his peaked hat. Then she ordered him to ride like the wind all the next night in search of the dwarf, and to bring back only his name.

RUMPLESTILTSKIN

"Tell me his name," she said, "and seven bags of money shall be yours. If you fail, then never return again!"

The messenger lost not a moment. All night he rode hither and thither, and this way and that. At last, a little before daybreak, he found himself at a cross-roads, where there is a mountain.

And not far beyond the cross-roads the messenger came to a little house that was round and had a roof of straw. Out of it there came the sound of singing. The messenger got down from his horse, crept near, and peeked carefully through the window.

Inside he saw a little man with thin legs, a long nose, and a rusty-red beard that spread down to his belt. He was dancing and singing before a fire that burned merrily on the hearth; and as he danced, these were the words he sang:

"This morn I baked, this night I brew—
 A wizard I, of mighty fame;
 But nobody ever, ever knew
 That Rumple—— is my name."

But listen as closely as he dared, the messenger could not be certain of the sound of the last two parts after that *Rumple*. But he knew that this must be the little dwarf the queen had sent him out to find. Rumple, Rumple—he was certain of that. But what then? *Stinzli? Stimpsky? Stitchken?*—he tried and tried, but he could not hear the last part of the name.

The messenger thought a moment, and then began making softly the call of a little owl. Sure enough, when the dwarf heard the owl calling, he began to sing and dance again. And as he danced, these were the words he sang:

> "Some live lone as fox and bird,
>   But who's to aid my Royal Dame?
> For nobody ever, ever heard
>   That Rumplestiltskin is my name."

At this, the messenger crept away from the window, and repeated the name he had heard over and over to himself, until he was as sure of it as of his own. Then he mounted his horse and galloped back to the palace.

THE LAST OF THE DWARF

The next day the queen went out into the orchard to await the coming of the dwarf. At the very stroke of noon he popped out as usual from behind the mossy old apple tree. This time

RUMPLESTILTSKIN 201

he wore a peacock's feather in his hat and carried a blanket in his hand.

"Ah-ha!" said he. "Three more guesses, ma'am, and the princess is mine." Because of his kindness to her, the queen pleaded with him, promising him any treasure except this one. But he grew angry and even uglier, and shouted:

"A bargain's a bargain; a vow's a vow
 To the very last word of it. Answer me now."

The queen smiled, and first she guessed, "Wheat-Straw."

He laughed.

Next she guessed, "Heaps of Gold."

He laughed louder. Then for her last and ninth guess the queen lifted her chin, laughed too, and whispered: "Now, how about *Rumplestiltskin?*"

The dwarf stared at her as if in a wink he had been turned to stone. Then he trembled all over with rage, and stamped on the ground.

"The witches must have told you! The witches must have told you! Oh, bother the witches!" screamed the little man, dancing with disappointment, as he hopped back to his little cottage, carrying the empty blanket. And the queen never saw Rumplestiltskin again.

NOTES AND QUESTIONS

1. Tell something to show that this story all happened in the world of "make-believe."

2. There are two main parts to this story. The first is "How the dwarf helped the miller's daughter." What is the second?

3. Here are some of the main points of the story, with others left out. Tell what points belong where (*a*), (*c*), (*e*), and (*g*) are.

(*a*)
(*b*) The king tells the girl she must spin gold.
(*c*)
(*d*) The girl promises to give the dwarf her baby.
(*e*)
(*f*) The messenger learns the dwarf's name.
(*g*)

RUMPLESTILTSKIN

4. Make a name, or title, for each of the three pictures in the story.

5. What other scene in the story would make a good picture?

6. In the picture on page 201, what shows that the dwarf expected to take the baby with him?

7. What did the dwarf mean when he said, "Three and three make six, ma'am"?

8. What did the miller mean when he said, "She's a lass in a thousand"?

9. On the dwarf's last visit, how did the queen make him feel sure that he was going to get the baby? She did two things. What were they?

10. For each picture in the story, find lines that tell what is happening. Be ready to read them.

11. Find lines that tell why the dwarf was willing to let the queen have nine guesses.

Three other stories everyone should know are "The Goblin of the Wood," Ingelow, and "The Maiden who Became a Spider," (in *Child-Library Readers, Book Four*); and "Canute Whistlewinks," Topelius (in *Canute Whistlewinks and Other Stories*).

A DOG OF FLANDERS

Louise de la Ramée

Most people like stories about dogs. Perhaps that is because dogs have been friends and helpers of men for thousands of years. This story will tell you what a true friend a dog will be to those who are kind to him.

THE OLD MAN, THE BOY, AND THE DOG

Nello and his dog Patrasche lived on the edge of a small village in a part of Belgium known as Flanders. The village was set in the midst of flat pastures and corn lands. It had a dozen or more houses, with shutters of bright green or sky blue and walls whitewashed until they shone in the sun like snow.

The little hut in which Nello and Patrasche lived belonged to old Jehan Daas, Nello's grandfather. In his earlier days he had been a soldier, but he had returned from the wars with a wound which had made him a cripple.

When Jehan Daas was eighty years old, his daughter had died and had left him her two-year-old son. He could hardly support himself, but he took the child gladly, and it soon became very dear to him. Little Nello—a pet name for

Nicolas—grew rapidly, and the old man and the child lived happily.

Their home was a plain little mud hut, but it was as clean and white as a sea-shell. It stood on a small piece of garden ground that gave the little family their beans, pumpkins, and other vegetables.

Jehan Daas and little Nello were poor, very poor. But the old man was gentle and good to the boy, and the boy was a truthful, kind-hearted child; and they were happy together.

Patrasche was their helper and their friend. Without Patrasche where would they have been?

For Jehan Daas was old and a cripple, and Nello was only a child. But Patrasche was young and strong. He was a dog such as one often sees in Flanders—with yellow hide, large head and body, and wolf-like ears that stood erect.

THE EARLY LIFE OF PATRASCHE

In his thirteenth month Patrasche had been sold to a hard-hearted peddler, who every day heaped his cart full of pots and pans and buckets, and made Patrasche draw the heavy load. The peddler himself walked along lazily by the side of the cart, smoking his black pipe. Happily for Patrasche, he was very strong. So he did not die, but lived on under hunger, thirst, and blows.

One day the dog and his master were going along the road that leads past the village in which lived Jehan Daas and Nello. It was a hot summer day, and Patrasche's cart was heavier than usual. His owner walked on without noticing the dog except to crack the whip at him.

Thus Patrasche struggled along on a scorching road. He had not eaten anything for twenty-four hours and had not tasted water for nearly twelve. Blind with dust, sore with blows, and weary with his load, the dog at last staggered and fell.

He fell in the middle of the white, dusty road, in the full glare of the hot sun. His master gave him kicks with his heavy wooden shoes and blows with his whip, but Patrasche did not move. He lay as if dead in the white summer dust.

After a while, finding his blows useless, the peddler thought that Patrasche was dead. So he took off the harness and kicked the dog aside into the grass. Then he pushed the cart lazily along the road.

JEHAN DAAS FINDS PATRASCHE

It was a busy road that day, and hundreds of people, on foot and on mules, in wagons and in carts, went by. Some saw the poor beast; most did not even look; all passed on.

After a time there came along the road a little old man who was bent and lame and very feeble. He saw Patrasche and paused. Then he knelt down in the grass and weeds of the ditch, and looked at the dog with eyes full of pity.

There was with the old man a little, rosy, fair-haired child, who toddled in among the tall weeds, and stood gazing upon the great, quiet beast. Thus it was that these two first met—the little Nello and the big Patrasche.

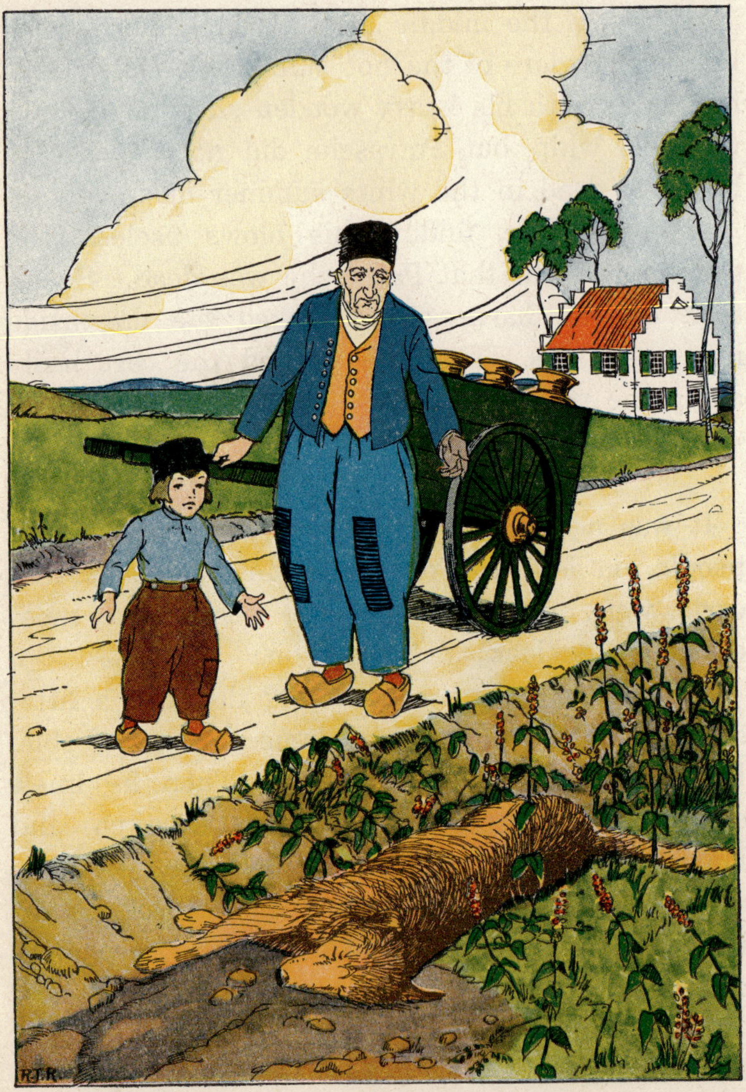
R.J.R.

Old Jehan Daas was a man with a kind heart. So he drew the sufferer to his own little hut, which was not far away. There he nursed the poor dog with such care that the sickness passed away. Health and strength returned, and finally came a day when Patrasche stood up again upon his four strong legs.

Now for many weeks he had been close to death; but all this time he had heard only the gentle sounds of the little child's voice and felt only the gentle touch of the old man's hand.

In his sickness they had grown to care for him— this lonely old man and the happy little boy. He had a corner of the hut, with a heap of dry grass for his bed; and they had learned to listen for his breathing in the dark night, to tell them that he was still alive.

When the dog was well enough to try a low, weak bark, the old man and the boy laughed aloud, and almost wept for joy. Little Nello, in delight, made chains of daisies and hung them around his neck.

So, when Patrasche arose, big and strong again, his great eyes had a look of happiness in them. In his heart he felt a mighty love, which was never to change. For Patrasche was grateful.

PATRASCHE BECOMES A FAITHFUL SERVANT

For some years Jehan Daas had earned his living by taking into a neighboring town the milk-cans of his neighbors. But pushing the cart in which the cans were carried was getting to be hard work for the old man. He was not strong, and the town was several miles away.

Patrasche watched the milk-cans come and go the first day after he was well. The next morning, before the old man had touched the cart, Patrasche arose, walked to it, and placed himself between the handles. He showed, as plainly as he could, his desire to work in return for the kindness he had received.

Jehan Daas pushed him away, for the old man thought it a shame to make dogs do hard work. But Patrasche would not be refused. Finding that they did not harness him, he tried to draw the cart with his teeth.

At last the old man gave way to the dog and allowed him to help him. He fixed his cart so that Patrasche could pull it, and this the faithful dog did every morning from that time on.

When winter came, Jehan Daas thanked the blessed fortune that had brought him to the sick dog in the ditch. For Jehan was very old, and was growing more feeble each year. He would not have known how to pull his load of milk-cans through the snow and the mud if it had not been for the grateful animal.

As for Patrasche, his new work seemed like play. After the heavy loads that his first master had made him draw, it was only fun to step out with this light cart and its brass cans, by the side of the gentle old man who always gave him a tender touch and a kindly word.

Besides, his work was over by three or four in the afternoon. After that time he was free to do as he wished—to stretch himself, to sleep in the sun, to wander in the fields, to romp with the young child, or to play with his fellow-dogs.

NELLO AND PATRASCHE DO THE WORK

A few years later, Jehan became so old that he could not go out with the cart any more.

Then little Nello took his grandfather's place beside the cart. He sold the milk and brought back the money to the owners with a pretty manner that charmed all who saw him.

The little boy was a beautiful child, with dark eyes and fair hair. Many an artist sketched the group as it went by—the green cart with the brass cans of milk, the great yellow-haired dog and the small figure that ran beside him, in wooden shoes.

Nello and Patrasche did the work so well and so joyfully together that Jehan Daas had no need to stir out. He could sit in the doorway in the sun, and watch the little boy and the dog go forth through the garden gate. While they were gone, he would doze and dream, and pray a little; and then he would awake again as the clock struck three, and watch for their return.

On their arrival at the hut, Patrasche would shake himself free of his harness with a bark of joy, and Nello would tell with pride the doings of the day. Then they would all go in together to their meal of rye bread and milk or soup. After twilight the boy and the dog would lie down together to sleep peacefully, while the old man said a prayer.

NOTES AND QUESTIONS

1. Why did Nello and Jehan take Patrasche home?
    (*a*) Because he could help them.
    (*b*) Because they wanted a dog for a pet.
    (*c*) Because they were kind-hearted.
2. How did Patrasche help?
3. Why was his help so valuable (*a*) in the following winter, (*b*) in later years?
4. Where else are dogs used to help men?
5. Be ready to tell in your own words—
    (*a*) Who Nello and Jehan Daas were.
    (*b*) How Patrasche happened to be lying in the ditch.
    (*c*) How Patrasche showed that he wanted to help.
6. If you know any other story of how a dog has helped his master, or done a faithful or brave thing, be ready to tell it to the class.

Three other good animal stories are "Casper, the Snow King," Stockton, and "Old Major, the Faithful Horse," Alcott (in *Child-Library Readers, Book Four*); and "Benjy in Beastland," Ewing (in *Child-Library Readers, Book Three*).

A BACKWARD LOOK

Now you have become acquainted with some very interesting people—Baucis and Philemon, Rumplestiltskin and the miller's daughter, old Jehan and little Nello. If someone asked you to tell one of these stories, which would you choose? Which of them tells of things that you think might really have happened, and which took place in the land of "make-believe"?

Sometimes we learn very valuable things from stories. As we read, we see just how people act and what happens to them because of what they do. Stories can teach us things as well as interest us. Which of these three tales teaches a very valuable lesson? What is the lesson? What people in one of the other stories did something that showed they had learned that valuable lesson?

Have you read any other stories that you think everyone should know? Perhaps you read some of those listed at the ends of the stories in this Part. Your teacher and your classmates would like to know the names of stories that you think they would enjoy.

If you liked what you have read in this part of your book, you would enjoy reading some of the books that are listed on pages 371-372. The librarian in your town will be glad to help you find these books in the library. They will give you many happy hours.

PART · V

BUSY WORKERS AND THEIR WORK

WE MUST WAKE AND WORK

So, away with sleep!
 Duties must be done
Ere the moments creep
 From us one by one!
  Only sluggards shirk!
  We must wake and work
With the sun!

—*Clinton Scollard*

HUNDREDS OF PEOPLE WORK FOR YOU

DID YOU ever stop to think that there are hundreds of people working for you every day? Perhaps you don't see how that can be true. Let us think a moment. That orange or apple or grapefruit you ate for breakfast—did it just drop from the tree on to your table? The wool in the clothes you are wearing—did you take it from the sheep and put it on? No. The fruit you eat comes to you because men and women have planted trees, picked the ripe fruit, and in other ways helped you to have it. Your clothes are the work of sheep-herders, sheep-shearers, cotton-pickers, cloth-makers, railroad men, and others.

Now do you see that there are really many, many people working for you? Yes, the world is full of workers. They are working that you and I may have food to eat, clothes to wear, homes to live in, and other things to make us happy and comfortable.

In this part of your book, you will read stories that tell how some of the world's work is done. First, you will be carried back to the time when our country was young, and you will see the busiest man of those days making something that meant greater comfort to thousands. Then you will visit groves of golden oranges, watch sheep losing their warm coats of wool, see some boys working faithfully so that they may have a playground, and last of all, sail out to capture some blackfish.

BENJAMIN FRANKLIN'S IRON STOVE
Carolyn S. Bailey

When our country was young, Benjamin Franklin was one of its greatest and busiest men. He ran a newspaper and a printing business, but they were not enough to keep him busy. So he started the first public library, the first fire-department, and the first hospital in America. These are just a few of the things he did. The story you will now read tells of another famous thing Franklin did, and how he happened to do it.

THE ARNOLDS' COLD HOME

Beth Arnold emptied the basket that her brother William had brought in. She stood in the light of a small open fire, a little Quaker girl of old Philadelphia. Her yellow curls were tucked inside a close-fitting gray cap, and her straight gray frock reached almost to the heels of her heavy shoes.

There was not a great deal in the basket—a little flour, some tea, a very tiny package of sugar, and some potatoes. Beth arranged them on the shelves in the kitchen, shivering a little as she moved about the cold room.

Philadelphia was a new city at that time, and the Arnolds had brought little with them from across the sea to make their lives cheerful. Outside, huge piles of snow were banked on the low stone doorsteps of the houses, and a chill wind blew up from the wharves. The Quakers who were out of doors hurried along with heads bent against the wind and their long cloaks wrapped closely around them.

In the Arnold house it was almost as cold as it was outside. The children's father had died since coming to the new country, and there were only Beth and William and their mother left to face this dreary winter. Mrs. Arnold did sewing, and William ran errands for the sailors down at the wharves, having his basket filled with food in return for his work. It was a hard winter for them, though; no one could deny that.

Mrs. Arnold drew her chair up to the fireplace now and got out her sewing. Beth leaned over her shoulder, watching the thin fingers trying to make the needle fly in and out of the white cloth.

"Your fingers are stiff with the cold!" Beth exclaimed, as she blew the coals with the bellows and then rubbed her mother's hands.

"Not very." Mrs. Arnold tried to smile.

"Yes, very," William said, as he swung his arms and blew on his finger tips. "We're all of us cold. It would be easier to work if we could keep warm."

FRANKLIN'S IRON STOVE 219

MR. FRANKLIN'S SURPRISE

Just then they heard a rap at their door. Beth ran to open it, and both children shouted with delight as a strange, slightly stooping figure entered. His hair was long and white, his forehead was high, and his eyes were deep-set in his long, thin face. His long cloak was folded about him as he reached out his hands to greet the family.

"Mr. Franklin!" their mother exclaimed. "We are most glad to see you. You are our very welcome guest always, even if our fire is very small and the house cold."

"A small fire is better than none," their guest

said. "Still," he looked at the children's blue lips, "I wish that your hearth were wider."

He crossed to the fireplace, feeling of the bricks and measuring with his eye the breadth and depth of the opening in the chimney. Then his face suddenly shone with a smile.

"What is it, Mr. Franklin?" Beth asked. "What do you see up in our chimney?"

"A surprise," the good neighbor of Philadelphia replied. "You will see that surprise before long."

He was gone as quickly as he had come, but he had left a glow of cheer behind him. All Philadelphia was warmed in this way by Benjamin Franklin. Whenever he crossed a doorstep, he brought comfort and helpfulness to the house.

"What do you suppose he meant?" Beth asked, as the door closed.

"I wonder," William said. Then he took out his speller and copy book, and the words of their visitor were soon forgotten.

But all Philadelphia soon began to wonder at the doings at the big white house where Benjamin Franklin lived. The neighbors were used to hearing sounds of hammering coming from the back where Mr. Franklin had built himself a workshop. Now, however, he sent away for a small forge

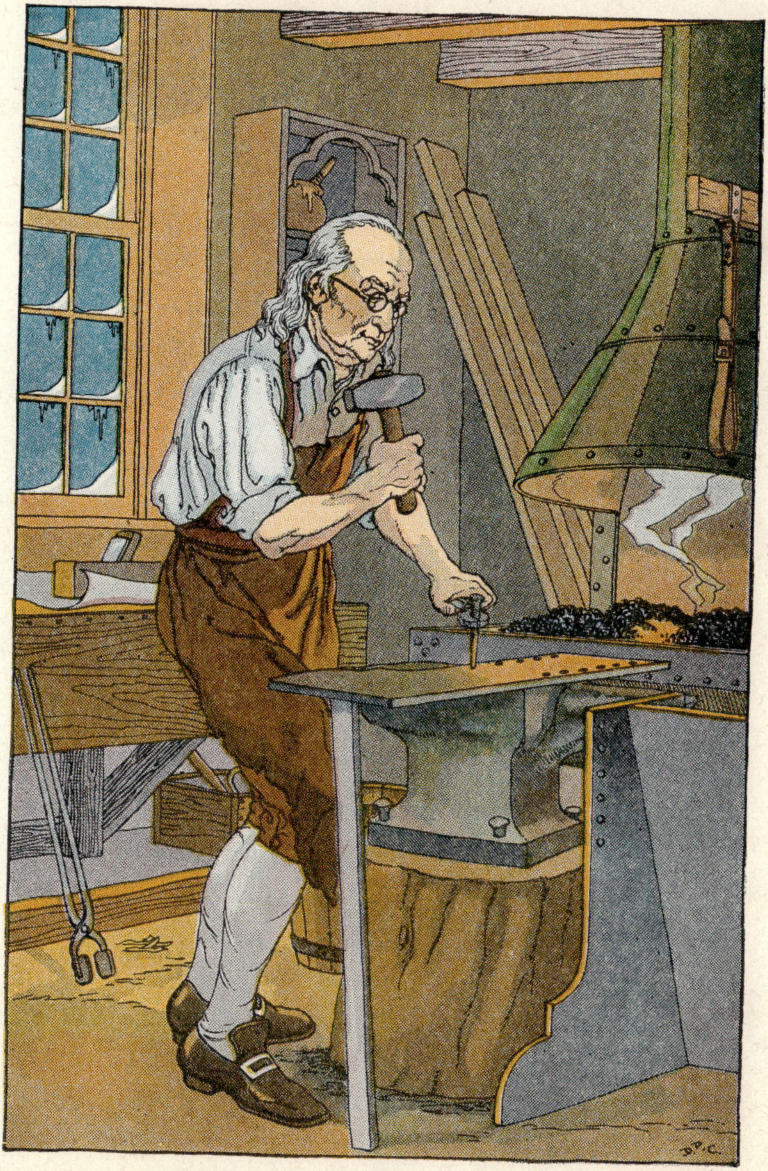

to heat iron. Red-hot iron is soft. It can be bent easily, and holes can be punched in it.

Soon the flying sparks of the forge could be seen and the sound of its bellows heard. Great slabs of iron were unloaded for him at the wharf, and for days no one saw him. He was shut up in his workshop, and from morning until night people heard ringing blows on iron coming from it as if it were the shop of some country blacksmith. No one could explain what Benjamin Franklin was doing, though.

THE FIRST IRON STOVE

In the middle of the winter Beth and William and their mother went to a friend's house to stay for a week. Mrs. Arnold was not well, and their house was very cold. The week for which they were invited became two, then three.

"We must go home," Mrs. Arnold said at last. "Mr. Franklin said that he would stop this afternoon and help William carry the carpet-bag. It is time that we began our work again."

As they took their homeward way through the snow, they noticed again the happy smile on Mr. Franklin's kind face. He held the handle of the bag with one hand and Beth's chilly fingers with the other. He was the spryest of them all, as they hurried on. They understood why when they opened the door of their home.

They started, at first, wondering if they had come to the wrong house. No, there, just as they had left them, were the rows of shining copper pans on the wall, the candlesticks on the mantelpiece, the warming pan in the corner, and the rag rugs on the floor. But the house was as warm as summer. They had never felt such comforting heat in the winter-time before. The fireplace was there, but it was indeed different. In it was an iron stove that kept the heat from going up the chimney and spread it out until the whole room was warm.

"That is my surprise," Mr. Franklin explained, as he saw the wonder and delight in the faces of the others. "It will keep the coals alive all night and not eat up as much fuel as your fireplace did. This is my gift to my dear friends, the Arnolds."

"Oh, how wonderful! How can we thank you for it? Now I shall be able to work!" the children's mother said.

Beth and William put out their hands to catch the friendly warmth of the fire in this, the first stove in the city of Philadelphia. It warmed them through and through. Then William examined it carefully so that he would be able to tend it. Beth bustled about the room, filling the shining brass teakettle and putting a spoonful of tea in the pot to make a cup for their mother and Mr. Franklin. At last she turned to him, her blue eyes looking deep in his. "You are so good to us," Beth said. "Why did you work so hard to make this iron stove for us?"

The kindest Friend that old Philadelphia ever had, stopped a second to think. At last he spoke in a gentle voice. "Because of your warm hearts, little Friend," he said.

FRANKLIN'S IRON STOVE

And so may we feel the kindly warmth of Benjamin Franklin's heart in our stoves, which are so much better, but which all began with the one he made for his neighbors in the Quaker City long ago.

NOTES AND QUESTIONS

1. Why did Franklin invent the iron stove?
    (*a*) to make money
    (*b*) to help others
    (*c*) to have something to do
2. Give three reasons why the stove was better than the fireplace. You can find these reasons in the part "The First Iron Stove."
3. Why did Franklin have to heat the iron when he was making the stove?
4. In what pictures are these things shown? Perhaps some of them are in two pictures. Your first answer is (*a*) *fireplace—219, 224.*

   (*a*) fireplace   (*e*) candlesticks   (*i*) iron stove
   (*b*) carpet-bag   (*f*) forge   (*j*) hammer
   (*c*) anvil   (*g*) rag rug   (*k*) cloak
   (*d*) andirons   (*h*) teakettle   (*l*) mantelpiece

Other stories you would like to read are "The Soap-Making of Remember Biddle," Bailey (in *Boys and Girls of Colonial Days*); "The Sampler," Turner (in *Magpie Lane*); and "The Postman Is a Happy Man," Wynne (in *For Days and Days*).

ORANGES, AMERICA'S GOLDEN HARVEST
Burchard Bacon

Perhaps you had an orange for breakfast this morning. It took you only a few minutes to eat it, but many people worked to help get it ready for you. Mr. Bacon, the author of this story, will tell you what happens to oranges after they ripen on the tree.

IN THE ORCHARD

"Mum-m-m-m," cried Jane, sniffing the air eagerly as they rode along. "Mother, what can that nice smell be?"

"It makes me think of orange blossoms," replied Mrs. Morgan slowly. "Perhaps we are near an orange grove. Oranges, you know, come to us from this warm, sunny land."

A moment later the automobile in which the Morgans were sight-seeing rounded a sharp curve in the road. There on one side of the road was an orchard of sturdy trees bearing green and yellow fruit. Here and there clusters of small white flowers could be seen among the dark shining leaves.

Mrs. Morgan asked the driver to go more slowly while she and Jane leaned forward to watch the men who were picking the fruit. The

ORANGES, AMERICA'S GOLDEN HARVEST 227

child heard the busy snip of the scissors which the men were using to cut the ripened fruit from its stems. The pickers carefully dropped the oranges from their gloved hands into wooden boxes piled near the trees.

PACKING AND SHIPPING THE FRUIT

But Jane wondered what happened to the oranges when they left the grove. Mrs. Morgan quickly arranged with the driver to take them to a large packing house. There Jane could see how the fruit was made ready to be shipped away on the railroad.

The packing house was a long shed with open sides built near a railroad track. Jane and her mother were shown inside the building, where they saw hundreds of boxes filled with the fruit just as it had come from the orchards in motor trucks and wagons. There was the faint smell of ripened oranges in the air. Jane watched the boxes of oranges as they were emptied one after another upon a wide, moving belt. This belt carried the fruit to the place where it was to be cleaned.

Jane and her mother followed the oranges, and saw them being dry-cleaned, that is, passed between rows of swiftly turning brushes. Next the oranges were carried on a belt to the room in which they were sorted out, or "graded," according to size.

The workers who were doing the grading sat in chairs on a high platform. Before them passed the oranges, on a wide, ever-moving belt. Three kinds of fruit the graders had to watch out for: decayed oranges, split oranges, and "culls." A cull is an orange that is too large or too small, or badly shaped or sunburned.

Quickly the graders rolled the fruit over with gloved hands. The decayed or split fruit was thrown aside. The culls were tossed upon a separate belt, which carried them away to be sold at a low price.

Jane felt her head whirl as she watched the wide, moving belts with their loads of jostling oranges. Suddenly she gave a little gasp of surprise. "Why, the oranges are disappearing!" she cried. And so they were.

"Each orange," said the guide, "as it travels along, finds an opening exactly its size. Through this opening it rolls down into a bin where a packer can easily reach it."

"Why, Mother," Jane exclaimed, "it's almost like the game I used to play! Don't you remember the little box I have at home, with tiny balls in it, that have to be shaken until they find the little nests that fit them?"

As the oranges rolled along, the small ones were the first to pass through the openings that fitted them, down into their bins. Then the medium-sized found their openings, and soon each bin was filled with oranges exactly the same size.

"And the last are the best of all in this game, aren't they?" cried Jane as she saw that only the large oranges were left. Having waited at ten or more stopping places for their smaller brothers to get out of the way, the big oranges finally passed through large openings and settled proudly into their own bins.

"No, indeed," said a worker; "strange as it may seem, the medium-sized oranges are the finest. They are sweeter and juicier. The big oranges spend their time growing big instead of sweet."

Next came the work of wrapping and packing, which was done by hand. Rows of packers, wearing gloves, stood beside the bins of graded oranges and worked rapidly. With one hand they seized a wrapping paper; with the other hand an orange. In the twinkling of an eye each orange was wrapped and placed, right side up, in a packing box.

"How many boxes can you pack in a day?" Jane asked one of the swiftest packers.

The busy fingers did not stop a moment as the worker answered: "Maybe ninety boxes, working nine or ten hours a day."

Now a box had been filled. In fact it looked to Jane as if it were too full. The box was lifted on to another moving belt, which carried it to the place where a cover was waiting for it.

Jane saw the lids being nailed on rapidly by a young man. As he put on each cover, he gave the box a sudden shake, drove the nails in—one, two, three, four—fastened a metal strap over the top, and put the box aside finished. All this he did in one minute.

Jane and the oranges said farewell to the packing house at the same moment. The boxes of fruit were wheeled across a narrow platform into a refrigerator car which was waiting on the railway track close to the entrance of the packing house. The little girl stood on the platform and saw hundreds of boxes piled into the train, and she knew that in New York or Massachusetts or Ohio or Wisconsin some other little girl would soon be eating a breakfast orange.

NOTES AND QUESTIONS

1. Below are some of the workers who handle the oranges. Put these workers in the right order. Number them 1, 2, 3, etc. Your first answer is *1. Pickers.*

  graders, truck-drivers, packers, pickers, box-nailers, car-loaders

2. Here is a list of seven things that are done to the oranges. Which are done by machine, and which are done by hand? Your first answer is (*a*) *Hand.*

  (*a*) Picked from the trees
  (*b*) Dry-cleaned
  (*c*) Moved about in the packing plant
  (*d*) Wrapped in paper
  (*e*) Graded according to kinds
  (*f*) Graded according to size
  (*g*) Packed in boxes

3. About how many boxes can a man pack in a day— fifty, one hundred ten, or eighty-five?

4. Which are the best oranges—the largest, the smallest, or the middle-sized?

5. Name a place in our country where oranges are grown. Perhaps you can name two places.

You would like to read "The Telegraph," "The Traffic Man," "Work Time and Sleep Time," and "Homes," Wynne (in *For Days and Days*).

SHEEP-SHEARING ON NANTUCKET ISLAND

ALICE CUSHING GARDINER AND NANCY CABOT OSBORNE

The three greatest needs of everyone are food, shelter, and clothing. For hundreds of years workers have grown crops for food, built houses to live in, and made cloth from wool and plants. Raising sheep for their wool is still an important work, just as it was on Nantucket Island when Mary and Peter were children.

GETTING READY FOR SHEARING DAY

The sheep on Nantucket Island were not kept in pastures, but on large open lands where they grazed in thousands. There were no shepherds to take care of them, for of course they could not run away; so the sheep roamed about eating what they could find, and became very ragged and dirty. They got along fairly well, for there were neither wild animals nor cruel dogs to harm them. Every year, on the second Monday in June, all the sheep were sheared.

During the week before shearing day the sheep were driven into the great pens beside a large pond, and on Saturday they were washed. On the following Monday, everyone on the Island had a holiday and went out to see the shearing and have some fun. They took their lunches with them, or bought them at booths and tents that were set up for the shearing.

Peter's Uncle Samuel owned many sheep. He always provided lunch for his shearers and his family in his own tent. Aunt Betsy, his wife, was busy all the week before, baking and roasting, and packing the good things into a trunk that was sent out on the morning of shearing day.

Mary was going to the shearing this year for the first time. Peter was to be allowed to leave the family as soon as they reached the grounds, and enjoy the day with his friends.

When Grandfather came home from the sheep-washing on Saturday night, the children asked him questions faster than he could answer them:

"Are all the tents up?"

"Are there any more sheep than there were last year?"

"Did anyone get tumbled over into the pond?"

"Yes, indeed," said Grandfather, "your Uncle Samuel went splash over backward! We couldn't help laughing."

Peter felt perfectly happy when Grandfather said, "Well, it will be a fine day tomorrow." That night he lay awake for hours, and then slept so hard that Grandfather had to call him in the morning.

"Peter, Peter, are you up?"

No boy ever dressed faster than Peter did that morning. Clatter, clatter, his stout shoes sounded on the stairs.

After breakfast, Grandfather and Peter walked down the street to the stable, harnessed the old white horse, and drove him back to the house. Mother and Mary were waiting at the gate with baskets of lunch beside them. Grandfather helped them into the cart, and climbed to his own seat; then off they went!

THE SHEARING

It was not long before they could see the flags flying over the tents, and then the tents themselves. When they reached the place where the horse was to be left, Grandfather turned to Peter, saying: "I can unharness alone; you run along and see the sights."

These were welcome words to the boy, who started off toward the sheep pens. His mother called after him: "Remember to come to your Uncle's tent for dinner at twelve o'clock!"

Peter turned and waved his hand to show her

that he heard; then he ran on to the place where Joseph and Benjamin Bunker were standing beside the shearing pens.

"Hi, Joseph!" he panted as he reached them.

"Hello," answered Joseph. "Come on; we're going to get near the fence to see the men shearing—they're at it now!"

A great crowd of men and big boys were pushing up to the outer fence of the sheep pen, and the smaller boys could not see past them. They could only hear the bleating of the sheep. However, by squeezing through the crowds, they managed to reach the fence, where a good-natured man made room for them.

On the left, they could see the pasture where the lambs were playing. The sheep were in the great round pen in front of the boys. Peter tried to count them, but he might as well have tried to count the waves in the harbor. A number of men were pushing among the sheep, sorting them out in a circle around the shearing space.

"There's Father shearing that black-faced sheep," exclaimed Joseph. "See, Ben, he's getting a lot of wool off her!"

Mr. Bunker always did his own shearing, for he did not own more than twenty sheep. No

237

shearer was more quick or sure than Mr. Bunker. Peter could see the heavy fleece falling upon the canvas which was spread on the ground, while Elijah, Mr. Bunker's helper, was carrying wool off to a table to be tied up.

"There! He's finished that one!" cried Ben, as Mr. Bunker stood up and wiped his forehead.

"My, that must be hot work!" exclaimed Joseph; "and there's Elijah letting out the next sheep. See, Peter, watch him throw her down!"

Mr. Bunker leaned forward, caught the sheep by one hind leg and gave her a push so that she sat down like a begging dog. The fleece was shorn from her stomach with a few quick clips of the shears. The boys watched spellbound as Mr. Bunker threw her down, first on one side and then on the other, to shear her back and sides.

The frightened creature soon looked very strange and naked; then she was pushed through a gate into the lambs' field. Out came the next sheep to be shorn, and then another and another.

"Well, I've seen as much of this as I want to," said Joseph, after a while. "Come on over and see what's going on at the big tent."

"I'd better go to Uncle Samuel's tent now," said Peter. "It must be nearly dinner time."

SHEEP-SHEARING ON NANTUCKET ISLAND

After dinner Peter and the other children left the tent and went to watch the lambs and their mothers. There was a great bleating and baa-ing, as one sheep after another was let out of the pen, looking very naked, and each finding her own lamb.

MARY FINDS A LAMB

"See that dear little thing!" said Mary, pointing to a poor little lamb in the corner that was bleating piteously. "Where can its mother be?"

"Oh, she'll turn up," answered Peter. "She probably hasn't been shorn yet."

But the afternoon wore on, the last sheep was shorn, and still the lamb was motherless. At last Uncle Samuel came along.

"Time to go home, children; step lively, now. We must get back by six o'clock."

Mary seized his hand. "Oh, Uncle, couldn't we do something about this poor little lamb? I think its mother is lost, and it will starve. Every single sheep has its lamb, and this little one is left. Couldn't we take him home with us?"

"Well, we'll have to ask Mother, Mary. Perhaps she will allow you to take it. I'll catch it for you."

Uncle Samuel climbed into the pen, walked slowly up behind the lamb, and took it in his arms.

It lay there quietly and only bleated once or twice as he carried it to the tent.

Mary's mother and Aunt Betsy were packing up the plates and cups, and the little that was left of the lunch.

"What have you there, Samuel?" exclaimed Aunt Betsy.

"A lamb that Mary wants to take home, if her mother will allow her."

"Oh, please, please, Mother, let me keep it," begged Mary. "I'll take all the care of it, and feed it every day. It hasn't any mother."

"It would be a good thing for Mary, if she would look after it herself," said Grandfather.

Mary was too happy to speak, but she squeezed

SHEEP-SHEARING ON NANTUCKET ISLAND

her mother's hand hard. Grandfather lifted the lamb carefully into the cart, and they started for home. All the way back Mary planned how she would take care of the lamb and bring it up to be a big sheep. Next year it would be shorn, and perhaps Mother could spare enough wool from it so that Mary could knit mittens for Father.

Notes and Questions

1. Give two reasons why shepherds were not needed on Nantucket Island.

2. When are sheep sheared—in the spring, early summer, or fall?

3. From the list below, choose the three main jobs in the work of sheep-shearing. Number them 1, 2, 3, in the order in which they were done.

Feeding the sheep　　Tying the wool into bundles
Washing the sheep　　Shearing the wool
Putting up the tents　　Driving the sheep into the pens

4. How long does it take a lamb to grow its first coat of wool for shearing? You can find the answer in something that is said near the end of the story.

5. What is the wool of a sheep called?

6. What else do you wear, besides wool clothes, that comes from an animal?

7. Name two other kinds of cloth besides woolen cloth.

Other interesting stories of how we get our clothes are "What the Boots Told David," and "Cotton, the Gift of the South," Paine (both in *Child-Library Readers, Book Four*); and "Cloth-Making in Pioneer Days," Watson (in *The Story of Textiles*).

EARNING A PLAYGROUND
Edward W. Frentz

Boys and girls must have places to play. The streets are often dangerous in this day of swift automobiles, and of course they do not make the best kind of playground. Sometimes older people are not as thoughtful as they should be in giving children playgrounds. This story tells how some boys who were willing to work for their fun won a playground, not only for themselves, but for all boys and girls who might ever live in their town.

Between the Long Road and the Cross Road near Brookvale lay a large three-cornered field, a part of the old Ross farm. Around it stretched an old fence, now only a post here and there, still holding together a few rails. Along the fence line had grown up a row of bushes almost as thick as a hedge. At the lower end of the field stood some tall old elm trees that kept it always shady. No other place in town made so good a ball field on a hot day.

But now some one had bought the old place, and the boys of the town had heard that the new owner was going to rebuild the fences, plow the fields, and make a real farm of it. So one day when they went over for their usual afternoon

EARNING A PLAYGROUND 243

game, they found a board nailed to one of the trees, and painted on it were the words, "Keep out, everybody."

"I guess it doesn't mean us," said Jimmy Hopkins. "We have always played here, and no one has ever stopped us."

"But it says 'Everybody,'" and Ben Hayes pointed to the sign.

"Well, let's try it, anyway," said one of the other boys, and so the game began.

It had been going on but a little while when

they heard a man's voice say, in a somewhat sharp tone, "Well, boys, I see you didn't read my sign." A tall old gentleman had stepped through a gap in the hedge and was looking at them out of a pair of keen blue eyes, half hidden by bushy gray brows.

"Yes, sir, we read it," said some one, "but we thought it didn't mean us."

"Oh! then you don't consider yourselves anybody. Is that it?"

"No, sir; we've always played here, and nobody ever said anything."

"But you see, I've bought the place now, and I must find a way to make it bring me in some money."

"Are you going to plow it up?" asked Eddie Brooks.

"Not just now, but it will keep a cow or two. That will pay me about five dollars a year."

The boys looked at one another. Not all of them together had so much money as that, or knew where or how they could get it. They were turning away, very downhearted at losing their playground, when Eddie spoke up quickly: "Could we do some work for you to pay for using this field?"

"You might, perhaps. Do you see this?" And he held up a blossom that looked like a tassel of silver-white silk. "It is a thistle, almost ripe. In a few days the wind would blow away every one of these tiny seeds. Every seed has a little balloon that would carry it a long way and drop it in some other field, to start a new crop. If you could keep this field clear of these thistles, I think I should feel that you had paid me about five dollars for the right to use it."

"We'll do it! Yes, sir! Of course we can," cried all the boys together.

"All right," said the old gentleman. "You may try it."

The boys worked hard at first, but after that it was easier, and before the month was out there was not a thistle to be found in the whole field. The old gentleman came out now and then and looked it over, and usually before he went away he would stop long enough to say, "Well, boys, are the thistles all gone? Good!"

One day the boys found their ball field nicely marked out by tiles set into the ground for bases, and under the elms were four stout benches. The old gentleman was sitting on one of them. "I thought," he said, "that perhaps your sisters might like to have some seats here. The work you boys did has paid for them."

That was the beginning of the Brookvale Playground. As the old gentleman grew older he used to spend more and more of his time sitting on one of the benches and watching the children at their games. Years later, when he died, it was found that he had given that field to the town, and had left money to care for it. On a

EARNING A PLAYGROUND

stone post at the lower end, where the big elms are, is a brass plate that tells in a few words how the first group of boys earned their right to use the field by clearing it of thistles.

NOTES AND QUESTIONS

1. Which one of these things the boys could have done do you think would have made the old gentleman feel most kindly toward them?
    (a) Offer to pay for the field from their savings.
    (b) Offer to work for the field.
    (c) Offer to get the money from their parents.

2. Why did the boys think that the sign did not mean them?

3. Below are four things that the old gentleman did. Which two make you believe that he liked children?
    (a) He let them work for the field.
    (b) He came often to see how they did their work.
    (c) He bought benches for the field.
    (d) He spent more and more of his time watching them play.

4. How was the old gentleman helping other people's fields as well as his own when he had the boys clear away the thistles?

5. How do thistle seeds get from one place to another?

ROB'S FIRST BLACKFISH DRIVE
Edward Morgan

Sometimes even a small boy or girl can do important work just as well as a grown man or woman. Rob Dunstan, just old enough to go on his first trip with the fishermen, proved that this is true. When the trip was over, Captain Jim said to him, "Some day you'll make the best fisherman in the whole village." Let's see what Rob did to make Captain Jim say that to him.

THE BLACKFISH COME AT LAST

Rob Dunstan and Charlie Fearing stood on the high bank above the beach one summer morning, looking out over the bay.

"I don't see a sign of blackfish," said Charlie.

"Neither do I," answered Rob. "I guess we might as well go home."

"Maybe there'll be a school of them tomorrow," said Charlie.

"Blackfish don't seem to be so plentiful as they used to be," said Rob sadly. "Why, my mother says she can remember the time when four or five schools came into the bay every summer; and last year there was only one."

Blackfish are really a small kind of whale,

from fifteen to twenty feet long. Although they are not useful as food, they are sold for a good price because of the oil contained in their fat.

The fish are captured in a strange way. They often swim in great schools along the top of the water very near the shore. At such times the fishermen row in boats just outside the school. Then the frightened fish, trying to escape the boats, will sometimes swim into very shallow water, where they are helpless and can easily be killed. This way of getting the fish upon the beach is called a "drive."

Last year, Charlie had helped in the drive, but Rob was too young. He had only watched it from the shore with the women and children. This year he hoped to take part in the drive himself if any fish came.

But now spring had gone by, and as yet there had been no sign of the blackfish.

One morning, about a week later, Rob was at work in the garden back of his mother's house, when he heard a shout from the shore. He listened a moment. "B-l-a-c-k-fish! B-l-a-c-k-fish!" was the cry.

Again and again other voices took it up, until the welcome news was spread all over the village.

Rob dropped his hoe and ran to the gate. Captain Jim, the best fisherman in the place, was just hurrying past.

"Can I go, Cap'n Jim?" he cried.

"Yes, Rob, there's a place in my boat. Run in and tell your mother, and don't waste any time. The boats are starting already."

Mrs. Dunstan had heard the cry and was coming down the path. She had also heard Rob's question and Captain Jim's answer.

"All right, Son, run along," she called out. "Don't get in the way of the men, and don't fall overboard."

Rob heard the first part of her words, but, before she had finished, he was running down the road after the big captain.

WHY ROB JUMPED OVERBOARD

When they reached the shore, most of the men had set off in their boats, and were trying hard to turn the great school of blackfish toward the land. More boats kept going out from the shore to help in the work. Soon there was a long line of boats beyond the fish, driving them toward the shallow water.

All the time the men were shouting. The boys who were old enough to be in the boats were told to make all the noise they could. Rob was yelling at the top of his voice. Captain Jim steered the boat, while four strong men rowed it, splashing the water with their oars. This shouting and splashing behind them frightened the blackfish and kept them swimming away from the boats.

Slowly the great school of fish was driven toward the land. Now they were moving along quietly, "like cows" as the fishermen say, not even trying to break through the line of boats.

They had almost reached the shore, when suddenly half a dozen blackfish turned and dashed for the open place between Captain Jim's boat and a smaller fishing-vessel that was next to it. If these fish were not turned back toward the shore, the others would follow them, and the drive would fail.

Rob was standing in the stern, near Captain Jim, who held the rudder. Quickly he saw that the escaping blackfish would pass close to the stern of the boat, and that the boat could not be stopped in time to head them off. In a flash it all happened. Rob leaped out almost in front of the fish! He sank out of sight, but came up at once. Keeping himself afloat with one hand, he splashed the water with the other. The great blackfish, frightened by the noise, turned again toward the shore, and the gap between the two boats was quickly closed.

Captain Jim stopped to pick up Rob and hauled him into the boat. He was not in the least hurt—wettings did not count at such times; it was midsummer, and there was yet plenty of work ahead that would dry him off.

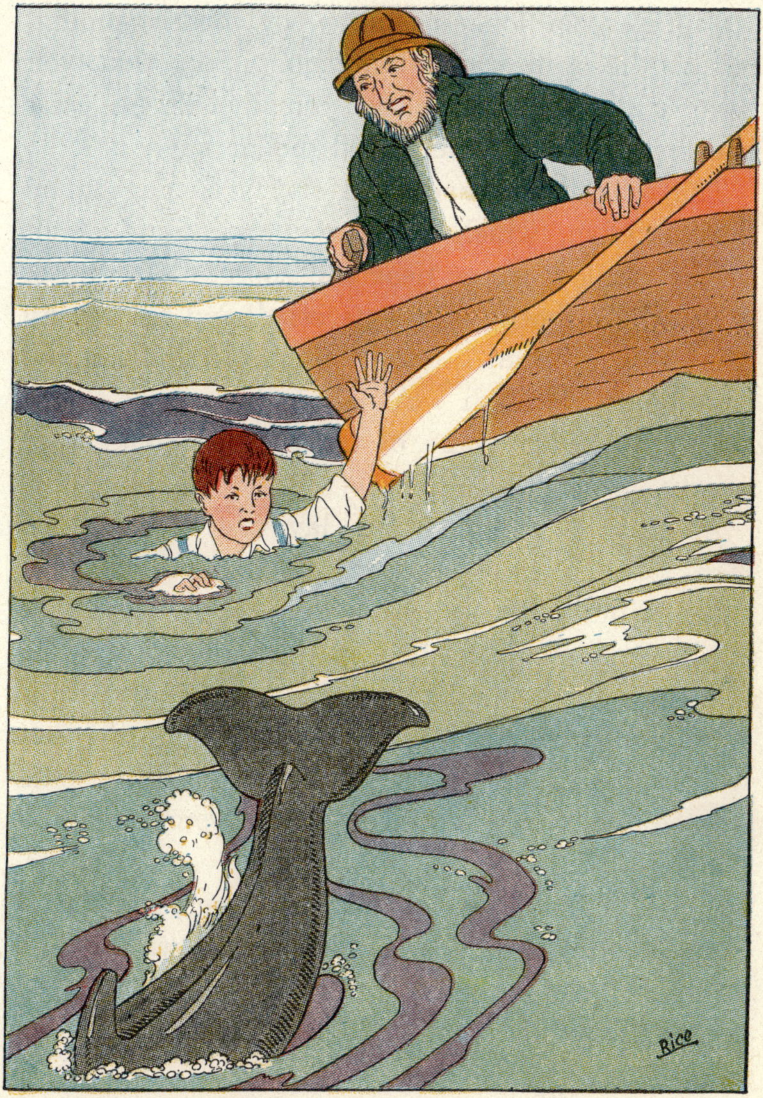
Rice

Captain Jim looked at the boy for a moment, but all he said was, "Remember, Son, that you haven't any father, and that your mother has only one boy." Not another word did he say.

The other boats had been slowly closing in on the blackfish, which were now swimming about in the shallow water near the shore.

"Start the work!" someone cried; and the killing of the fish began. Round and round went the frightened blackfish. As their tails lashed the water into foam, some of the smaller boats were nearly upset.

At last all the blackfish lay motionless. The men and the boys tied ropes to them and pulled the fish out of the water to the beach. Hundreds of the small whales now lay upon the sand. The blackfish drive was over.

Men were selected to see that none of the fish were stolen during the night; and the boats started for their landing-places. Tomorrow the fish would be sold.

"You might as well run along home, Rob," said Captain Jim, as the boat touched the shore. "You've been working pretty hard today, and you're all wet." That was all he said.

ROB'S FIRST BLACKFISH DRIVE

But as Rob started on a brisk run up the road, he heard the Captain call out: "You stopped those fish like a man. Some day you'll make the best fisherman in the whole village."

Notes and Questions

1. Why did Captain Jim think Rob would some day be a great fisherman? Choose the two best reasons.
    (a) He was strong.   (c) He was a quick thinker.
    (b) He could swim.   (d) He had courage.

2. Tell what words are missing in sentences (a), (b), and (c).
    (a) A large number of fish swimming together is called a ....
    (b) Blackfish are small ....
    (c) Blackfish are useful for their ....

3. What was the main work of the people in Rob's village? Give one reason to prove your answer. Perhaps you can give two reasons.

4. How did the boys help (a) in the boats, (b) after the fish were killed?

5. How many blackfish were there — several hundred, about one hundred, or several thousand?

6. Be ready to tell in your own words what blackfish are and how they are captured.

7. Be ready to tell why Rob jumped overboard. Be sure you make clear just how the fishermen were in danger of losing the fish.

Another good fishing story is "Trawling," Whiteman (in *Jane and Jerry*).

A BACKWARD LOOK

You have just read four stories that told you how some of the work of the world is carried on, and you read of a very useful job that some boys did. Which story had to do with food? Which with clothing? One of the stories showed you a man inventing something. Which one was it? Do you know of any other great inventor and what he has invented? Which work that you read about calls for the greatest courage? Which story showed you some machines that save labor?

It would be interesting to make a list of workers who help you to be comfortable and happy. For example, who are the different workmen needed to build a house? Who help to keep your house warm?

There are many stories you would enjoy reading about the work of the world and how it is done. Some of the things you use carelessly every day come from places and are made in ways that would surprise you. From where does the rubber come for your boots and bicycle tires? Of what is the glass for your windows made, and how is it made? Does silk grow on plants like cotton?

These are just a few of the interesting things to learn about the work-a-day world. Perhaps you have discovered other workers that this part of the book did not tell about. Some of the books named on page 373 will tell you about more workers who help to supply your needs.

PART · VI

FAMOUS HEROES OF LONG AGO

LONG AGO AND FAR AWAY

Long ago and far away,
All the good things were, they say—
Silver knights and castles gold,
Ladies fair and witches old,
Banners, trumpets, glad array,
Long ago and far away.

Long ago and far away—
Wish that good time were today—
Dragons lived in caves of glass,
Never let a brave knight pass,
If his armor was not on.
All good things are past and gone,
Long ago and far away—
Now a boy can only play.

Oh, to live in that far day,
Long ago and far away;
Fight the dragon till he bled,
Carry off his tail and head,
Kill the old witch in her lair,
Rescue babes and ladies fair—
'Twas the tale of any day,
Long ago and far away.

—*Annette Wynne*

Reprinted by permission from *For Days and Days; A Year-round Treasury of Verse for Children*, by Annette Wynne. Copyright, 1919, by Frederick A. Stokes Company.

EVERY LAND HAS ITS HEROES

EVERY nation has its heroes—brave, unselfish men and women who have risen to help the people in time of trouble. These great heroes are never forgotten. They are ever loved and honored for the good and brave deeds they have done. We Americans will never forget such men as George Washington and Abraham Lincoln.

Now your Book Comrade will tell you some stories of famous heroes who lived hundreds and hundreds of years ago. They lived long before men knew how to print books, but their great deeds were kept alive by wandering story-tellers called minstrels. These minstrels went about the country telling tales or singing songs of mighty warriors. They learned these tales from older minstrels. Of course, as they told the stories over and over, the minstrels added things that they imagined might have happened.

Thus the stories were passed on through the years until finally someone wrote them down on paper. Then people began to read them.

Three of the greatest of these world heroes are Beowulf, Sigurd, and Roland. As you read of their brave deeds, just as they were told by wandering minstrels, could you make a play in which some of these heroes appear?

BEOWULF, THE BRAVE PRINCE
Clara E. Lynch

The story of the famous deeds of Beowulf was first written down in a long poem about one thousand years ago. But hundreds of years before this poem was written, minstrels in Denmark and Sweden told and sang the story of the great hero. As you read the story, try to find out why Beowulf was so loved by all.

KING HROTHGAR'S HALL

Many, many years ago, a king named Hrothgar ruled over the Danes. This king was a very brave man and won many battles when he went to fight against his enemies. He was ever thinking what he could do to make his people happy, and they loved him greatly.

King Hrothgar decided to build a splendid hall, larger and more beautiful than had ever been seen before. So he called his workmen and said: "Build me a hall, great and wide, and when it is built, I will call all my brave warriors into it and give them rich presents."

So the hall was built, and the king made a great feast for his warriors. To each of them he gave a ring of gold, because they had fought so bravely. Then he told them that they must come to this beautiful building every evening, and tell stories and sing and feast together.

This pleased the men, and they were sure that no other land in all the world had a king who did so much for his people. So every night the great fires roared on the hearth. The warriors sat at the long tables and feasted, while the minstrel played upon his harp and sang to them of great deeds.

Far out on the wild lands lived a wicked giant named Grendel. Every night as he saw the bright light shine out from the hall and heard the laughter and shouting, he was angry because the Danes gathered there were so happy. At last one dark night he crept into the hall and killed thirty warriors.

Then there was great sorrow among the Danes, and the good king wept for his men. After this the Danes would not stay in the hall at night. There was no more singing or telling of stories. No one dared to fight a giant who was so strong that he could snap iron bars in two and break down the thickest doors.

When Grendel found that the warriors would not enter the hall at night, he lay waiting in dark places and seized them as they passed. So for twelve long years the Danes suffered from their terrible enemy. During all this time, no sounds of laughter or song came from within the great building. It was silent and dark, for Grendel was the only one who walked there.

THE COMING OF BEOWULF

The years passed, and no man was found who was strong enough to fight with Grendel.

Now it happened that far away in the land of the Goths, a brave prince named Beowulf heard the story of the wicked giant. His heart was filled with pity for the Danes. "I will go across the sea and slay this wicked giant," he said. "I will save King Hrothgar and his people from the terror and suffering which have fallen upon them."

Taking with him fifteen brave warriors, Beowulf set sail for the land of the Danes. For two days they sailed, and then they came to a place where steep cliffs rose out of the sea. High above them they saw a man guarding the shore.

Waving his spear, the man cried, "Who are you who come to this shore, armed with swords and shields? I must know, or you cannot pass, for you may be enemies of our king."

Beowulf answered, "We are Goths, and we come as friends to this land. We have heard that there is a terrible enemy among the Danes, and I have come to help King Hrothgar."

"If you have come to help us, you are indeed welcome," said the guard. "Follow me, and I will lead you to the king."

Beowulf and his companions climbed up the rocky path and followed their guide until they could see a huge building. Then the guard stopped. "There is the great hall," he said, "and there you will find the king. I will go back to the cliff and watch, for now you cannot miss the way."

So the Goths marched forward until they came to the hall. At their knock, a servant came out and asked from what country they had come. Beowulf answered, "My name is Beowulf, and I come from the land of the Goths. I will tell my story to King Hrothgar himself, if he will listen to me."

"I will ask the king and quickly bring you word," said the servant, bowing low.

Now King Hrothgar was old and gray-haired, and as he sat in his beautiful hall, his heart was sad. He thought of all his brave men who had been killed by Grendel, and he wondered if he would ever find a hero strong enough to free his people from this wicked giant.

As he thought of these things, the servant came and knelt before him. "My lord," he said, "strange men have come from far beyond the sea, and they wish to speak with you. Their leader is called Beowulf, and he seems to be a mighty prince. I pray you, refuse them not."

At these words the king started up. "God has sent us a brave warrior who will slay the wicked Grendel," he cried. "I knew Beowulf when he was a boy, and now men say he has the strength of thirty men. Tell the warriors to enter, and say to them that they are welcome to the land of the Danes."

Soon Beowulf and his companions stood before Hrothgar, and Beowulf told the king why they had come to the land of the Danes.

"I heard in my own country of the terrible Grendel, who kills your brave warriors. Men say that he cannot be hurt by weapons; so I have come to fight him without sword or shield. I will try to save the Danes from this wicked giant."

These brave words filled the king with joy. "O Beowulf," he said, "if you will slay Grendel, our great hall will again become a place of laughter and song."

Then Hrothgar ordered rich food and drink to be placed upon the tables, and the Goths and the Danes sat down together. While they feasted in the beautiful hall, the minstrel sang sweet songs praising Beowulf, who had come so far across the sea to save them.

When the sun had set and darkness was falling, the king rose to leave the hall. "Beowulf," he said, "keep guard over this house tonight. Save us from our terrible enemy, and whatever you ask shall be given you."

Then all the Danes left the hall, but Beowulf and his companions waited for the coming of Grendel.

BEOWULF, THE BRAVE PRINCE

BEOWULF'S BATTLE WITH GRENDEL

As the darkness came on, Beowulf prepared for the battle, taking off his armor and laying aside his sword and shield. Then he said to his men, "This night shall prove whether Beowulf or Grendel is the stronger. With my two hands I shall fight the giant. I have said that I will fight this battle alone, and I must keep my word, even though I die in this hall."

Then all the Goths except Beowulf lay down to sleep. But Beowulf kept guard, watching for the terrible giant.

All at once the great doors burst open, and Grendel entered the hall. He looked around at the sleeping warriors and then quickly stretched out his arm to seize one of them. He did not see Beowulf, who was quietly watching him. Suddenly the giant's arm was caught in a grasp so strong that he could not shake himself free.

Then a terrible battle began. Backward and forward they struggled until the great hall shook. Grendel had thought no man dared touch him, and his anger was fierce when he found he could not free himself from Beowulf's hand. The noise of the battle was heard far away. The Danes woke and knew that the brave stranger was fighting to save their land. Louder and louder grew the noise, and fiercer grew the struggle.

But at last the giant knew that Beowulf was too strong for him. He was so terribly wounded that he could fight no longer. With a great cry, the giant turned and rushed from the hall. On and on he ran through the forests until he came to the shore of a dark lake. Into this lake Grendel plunged and was never seen again.

When morning came, the glad news was told everywhere. "Grendel is dead! Grendel is dead! The noble Beowulf has saved our land!" the Danes cried joyously to one another.

The king and queen, dressed in their most beautiful robes, came forth to meet Beowulf. Stretching out his hands to the brave prince, the king said, "O Beowulf, from this time, I will love you as a son. And now ask whatever you wish, and I will give it to you."

"Not for reward did I come to your land," said Beowulf, "but to save you from this terrible giant. Now that Grendel is dead and will nevermore trouble you, I shall joyfully return home."

After this a great feast was spread in the hall, and the Danes and the Goths sat down together. The hall was filled with laughter and song. When the feast was over, the good king gave Beowulf a banner, a helmet, and a sword with a handle of twisted gold. Then eight beautiful horses were led up to the door as a gift to the great hero. Their harness was all of gold, and upon one of the steeds was a saddle decorated with silver. This was the saddle upon which King Hrothgar himself had often ridden to battle, and he gave it to Beowulf.

To the other Goths the king also gave rich presents. Then the music and feasting went on until late in the night, for the Goths were soon to sail for their home.

THE SECOND MONSTER

But something happened that kept Beowulf and the other Goths still longer in the land of the Danes. In the dark lake lived another terrible monster. One night soon after Grendel had died, this monster came up out of the lake and entered the hall where the Danes lay asleep.

Suddenly a cry rang through the building. When the men started up and seized their swords, the monster fled, but the Danes found that one of their bravest warriors had been killed. Then there was great mourning in the hall, and messengers were sent to tell the sad news to the king.

"Oh, if Beowulf had only been there!" cried Hrothgar, when he heard what had happened.

Some of the men then ran to wake Beowulf, who was asleep in the king's palace. Surprised at the sudden call, Beowulf and his warriors hastened to the king.

"Oh, Beowulf," said Hrothgar, "a great sorrow has come to us. A monster from the lake has killed one of my bravest companions!"

"Do not weep, O King," said Beowulf. "Let me see the track of this monster and give me one day, and I promise to slay this enemy, also."

Following the tracks, Beowulf and the king came

BEOWULF, THE BRAVE PRINCE

to the shore of the dark lake. Then the great hero once more made ready for battle. He put on his coat of steel and his helmet, which no blade could cut. In his strong right hand he carried his gleaming sword.

Standing on the shore of the lake, Beowulf turned to the king. "Now, O King, I am ready," he said. "If I do not return, I pray you be a friend to my warriors and send the gifts which you gave me to my king. Then he will know that I fought bravely."

Before Hrothgar could answer, Beowulf plunged into the water. Down, down he went into the dark lake.

THE BATTLE UNDER THE WATER

The monster saw Beowulf coming, and lay waiting for him. As soon as he touched the bottom, she sprang upon him and seized him in her terrible claws. Only his armor saved the hero from death in that fierce grasp. When she found that the armor could not be broken, she dragged him off to her cave.

There, deep down under the waters, Beowulf fought the hardest battle of his life. Backward and forward struggled the hero and the monster, in and out of the cave.

At last Beowulf felt that his strength was leaving him. At this moment the brave hero saw a great sword hanging on the wall of the cave. Never before had he seen such a weapon. Surely no one but a giant had ever used it. Seizing the sword, Beowulf lifted it high above his head, and struck with all his might. Instantly the monster fell dead. Then a strange thing happened. The blade of the sword melted away, and only the hilt was left in his hand.

Looking about him, Beowulf saw piles of gold and silver on every side. He gazed in wonder at the treasure, but he did not touch it. He had gone down into the lake to save the Danes from their terrible enemy. He had won the victory, but he would not make himself rich with the evil monster's gold.

One thing only did Beowulf take from the cave. He still held in his hand the hilt of the wonderful sword. This he would take to King Hrothgar, and together they would read the strange writing on the twisted gold. So up from the dark lake came Beowulf, and back he went to the king's palace.

The king and queen came forward to meet him, and all the warriors crowded around. When Beowulf had told of his battle under the water, he gave the hilt of the sword to Hrothgar. All around the hilt was written a story which told that the sword had been made for a giant, hundreds of years before.

Beowulf told of the strange animals that made their homes in that dark lake. He told also of the piles of gold and silver which lay in the cave. "But I touched nothing of the treasure. Not for gold did I go down into that dark lake, but to save the people of this land," he said.

At these words the Danes shouted and cheered in their love for this brave hero. Never had men heard such a story as this which Beowulf told.

"O Beowulf," said the king, "you are a true warrior. Your name shall be known everywhere for your brave battles."

Then Hrothgar commanded that a feast be prepared. Beowulf sat at the king's right hand, and all were happy. Now everyone could enter the beautiful hall without fear.

BEOWULF'S RETURN TO HIS HOME

Beowulf's work in the land of the Danes was now done, and he was eager to return home. Calling his warriors, he went with them to the king to say farewell, and to thank him for the rich gifts he had given them.

"If ever again I can help you, my lord, I will come to you with joy," said Beowulf.

The old king thanked Beowulf and gave him more beautiful gifts than before. Then he put his arms around the hero's neck and kissed him, for he loved him greatly. The Goths then marched down to their boat and sailed for home.

When they touched the shore of their own land, the king welcomed Beowulf joyously, saying, "Sit here beside me and tell me all that has happened since we parted."

So Beowulf told of the kindness King Hrothgar had shown him. He told of the beautiful hall which no one had dared to enter at night, of his fight with Grendel, and of the terrible battle under the water.

Then Beowulf laid before the king the gifts which had been given him. The eight beautiful horses with their harness of gold were led up to the door, and he gave these also to the king. Of all the gifts which Beowulf had received from the Danes, he kept none for himself.

After this the people loved Beowulf more than ever. For though he was such a mighty warrior and so strong in battle, yet he loved to do good and to live in peace with all. And though he had won great battles, yet he was never proud or boastful.

Notes and Questions

1. Why did Beowulf fight the monsters?
   (a) To win rich rewards.
   (b) For the sake of adventure.
   (c) To help people in trouble.
2. Tell something about Beowulf to show that he was
   (a) brave   (b) unselfish   (c) kind-hearted
3. Put these main happenings in the right order so that they make an outline of the story.

   > The battle with the monster in the lake
   > The coming of Beowulf
   > Beowulf's return to his home
   > The sorrow of the Danes
   > The battle with Grendel
   > The coming of the second monster

4. (a) Which battle did Beowulf win by his own strength?
   (b) In which battle did he get some unexpected help? What was it?

5. Be ready to read lines that tell about the pictures on pages 260 and 266.

6. Find lines that best tell what kind of man Beowulf was. Be ready to read them.

7. Be ready to tell in your own words any of the main happenings of the story given in Question 3 above.

In *Stories of Great Adventures,* by Bailey, you will find another story of Beowulf that you would enjoy reading.

SIGURD, THE YOUNG WARRIOR

Clara E. Lynch

Sigurd was such a great hero to the people of Europe that many countries claimed him as their own. In some places he is known as Siegfried. Like Beowulf, he had strange and wonderful adventures.

SIGURD'S CHILDHOOD

Long, long ago, in the palace of good King Alf of Denmark, there lived a little boy named Sigurd. Sigurd's father had been a great warrior and had died in battle. When King Alf heard of this, he felt so sorry for Sigurd's mother that he asked her to come with her little boy and live in his palace.

So she came to live in the palace of King Alf. Here she and the little Sigurd were welcomed very kindly, and everyone tried to make them happy. The boy could not remember his father, and he grew up in this beautiful home feeling the love of a son for King Alf.

Sigurd's mother told him many wonderful stories about his father. She told how strong and brave he had been, and how he had always told the truth, even to his enemies. She told Sigurd of his father's wonderful sword, which would cut through iron or stone. In the last battle he had fought, the sword had been broken, but she had picked up the pieces from the battlefield.

As Sigurd grew older, he loved more and more to hear these wonderful stories about his father.

"Mother, will you give me my father's sword?" the eager boy would often ask.

"Not yet, my Sigurd; you are too young," his mother would say.

"But, Mother, I am big and strong," the boy would answer.

Then his mother would smile lovingly at Sigurd.

"Wait a little, my Sigurd. You are still only a boy. Your father was a hero. Much there is for you to learn before you can wear his sword!"

"But, Mother, if you would give me the sword I would be a hero, too, for then I would go away from here and do some great deed!"

"Stay with your mother, now, Sigurd. Be brave and true. Think not of yourself but always of others. Then, some day, you shall do great deeds."

The years passed, and Sigurd grew taller and stronger. His hair was golden, his cheeks were rosy, and his eyes were large and shining. Other children loved him because he was unselfish, and everyone in the palace was proud of the beautiful boy who always spoke the truth and who was afraid of nothing.

REGIN THE SMITH

In King Alf's palace lived a very old man named Regin. He was so old that no one knew when he had come to live there. Regin was the greatest smith in the world. He made spears, swords, and armor such as no other man could make. He made wonderful things of gold and silver, also, and Sigurd loved to run into the smithy and watch Regin at his work.

Regin was a very wise man and could play sweetly upon the harp and sing wonderful songs of heroes and their battles.

But Regin was very unhappy, because many

years before, a great treasure had been taken from him. Always he was thinking and planning how he could get it back. He did not need the gold, for the kings had given him rich presents; yet day and night he thought of his loss.

Now Regin knew that a battle must be fought to win back his treasure, and he himself was not brave enough to fight. So year after year he watched for someone who would get the treasure for him. When he saw Sigurd growing up brave and strong, he thought, "This boy has great strength and is afraid of nothing. He shall fight my battle and win my treasure for me!"

So Regin went to King Alf and said that he would like to teach Sigurd, and give him skill in making swords and armor.

The king looked at Regin a moment and then said: "O Regin, truly you are very wise, and it would be well for the boy to learn some things from you. But he is loving and truthful, and I would keep him so. You love no one. You would deceive even me, your king and your friend. Teach Sigurd, if you wish, but teach him not to hate and lie."

Regin answered in a low voice: "Have no fear, O King. This boy will never lie, and his heart

SIGURD, THE YOUNG WARRIOR

will always be full of love. But great deeds shall he do in the years to come, and the whole world shall hear the name of Sigurd!"

After this Sigurd spent part of each day with Regin, who taught him many things which a prince should know. When his hours of study were over, the boy would hurry away into the forest to play with the other children.

In the woods Sigurd was only a happy child without any thought of battles or heroes. The forest rang with the shouts of the children at their play, and often Regin heard the gay laugh of the young prince. Then Regin would say to himself: "The time is near when I can use the boy. I must not wait too long. When he is older, he may want the treasure; but now he cares not for the gold. If he wins it, he will give it to me."

One day Regin played upon the harp and sang wonderful songs to Sigurd, until the boy's eyes shone as he listened. The songs were all of battles and heroes, and the heroes were Sigurd's own father and grandfather.

Then Regin said: "When will you do great deeds? Will you stay forever here, where the people are cowards and where the king is too lazy to fight?"

Sigurd frowned at these words. "The people of this land have been kind to me," he said. "They are not cowards. And I love the good king. Why should he fight when his land is happy and when no enemy has come against him?"

Regin laughed as he answered, "Do heroes wait for the enemy to come to them? Do they not ride forth and win great victories? But this king is not a hero, and you will stay at home with him, for you do not care to do great deeds!"

"You know that I care, Regin! Some day I shall ride away from here and win a great victory."

"Then why do you not ask the king to give you a horse?" said Regin.

"I have a horse and everything that I need," answered Sigurd. "Why should I ask for more?"

"But you have no war-horse," said Regin. "Ask the king to let you choose a war-horse from the horses running free in the meadow."

SIGURD'S HORSE

That evening Sigurd said to King Alf, "Will you give me a horse which I may ride to battle?"

"Where will you go to battle?" asked the king.

"I do not know. But the time is coming when I must do great deeds, and I wish to be ready."

SIGURD, THE YOUNG WARRIOR

"Take whatever horse you wish, Sigurd," said King Alf, kindly.

Early next morning Sigurd went out to the meadow where the horses were grazing. Suddenly an old man dressed in gray stood before him. "What do you wish, Sigurd?" asked the stranger.

"I wish to choose a horse," answered the boy. "But how do you know my name?"

"I knew your father," said the old man. "He was a brave warrior, and I loved him."

"I know that you are wise, and I love you because you loved my father," said Sigurd. "Will you help me choose my war-horse?"

"Yes," said the old man. "Let us drive these horses into the river."

Sigurd thought that this was a strange way to choose a war-horse, but he did as he was told, and soon the horses were in the water. All but one quickly struggled back to the shore. This one, a beautiful gray steed, swam to the other side and bounded away. Then turning suddenly, he ran back into the river and swam to Sigurd's side.

"Here is your horse, Sigurd," said the old man. "Strong and swift is he, and on his back you shall ride to great victories. Only think not of yourself nor fear for your life!"

Before Sigurd could thank him, the stranger had gone. The beautiful gray animal stood as if waiting for his master to mount him. The happy boy sprang upon his back and rode toward the palace.

"You have chosen a splendid steed, my son," said the king when Sigurd reached the palace. "He will be strong and swift. But why did you choose this one from among all the horses in the meadow?"

Then Sigurd told of the strange old man who had met him near the river.

The good king looked lovingly at the boy and asked, "Did he say anything of the time when you shall ride away from us?"

"He only told me that I should not think of

myself nor be afraid, if I wished to do great deeds," said Sigurd.

"You will do great deeds, my Sigurd, but there is time enough," said the king, "for you are still young."

REGIN'S STORY

So the days passed, and Sigurd rode his splendid horse and worked at the forge and was happy always. One day when he sat in the smithy, Regin told him stories of heroes who had fought many battles and had at last become kings.

Then Regin said, "You are the son of a noble warrior. Why do you remain here, when there are great deeds to be done?"

"Some day I shall do great deeds, Regin," said Sigurd. "But I am not yet old enough. Why do you say these things to me?"

"Because a great deed is waiting now for you to do," answered Regin. "But I shall say no more, for you love the pleasant, easy life in the palace. The life of a hero is hard. Your father suffered and was often cold and hungry. But his son is not like him!"

Sigurd's eyes flashed, as he sprang up from his seat.

"Tell me now, Regin!" he cried. "What is the

deed I must do? You know that I am not afraid of cold or hunger or pain!"

"Sit down, Sigurd, and I will tell you," said Regin. "Many hundreds of years ago I built for my father a great castle, and in this castle my father gathered his treasure. I longed for my share of the gold, but my father would not give it to me.

"So I worked and waited, but I thought of the gold all day and dreamed of it all night. Then my father died, and I thought that at last I would have a share of the treasure; but my brother drove me from the house, saying that the gold belonged to him.

"Years after that a terrible dragon seized the castle and the gold. This dragon has killed so many men that no one will live in that land. But now you have come, O Sigurd, and I know you will kill the dragon and win the treasure. Many, many years have I waited for this day. Will you do this deed and win the praise of men?"

Then Sigurd looked straight at Regin with his clear, honest eyes.

"Yes," he said, "I will go at once and do this deed. But the gold is evil. It has brought unhappiness to many. It made your father selfish, and it made your brother wicked. Because of it, you hated your brother. Because of it, this wicked dragon has killed many good men. Not for the sake of the gold will I go and do this deed, but to rid the world of the terrible monster!"

SIGURD'S SWORD

The next day Sigurd came to the smithy and said to Regin, "You have given me a great work to do. Now I have something to ask from you."

"Ask whatever you wish, Sigurd, and I will do it for you," said Regin.

"Make me a sword, good and strong, from the pieces of my father's old sword."

Regin smiled and answered, "Bring me the pieces, so that I can weld them together."

Sigurd went to his mother and said, "Mother, where are the pieces of my father's sword which you have kept for me all these years?"

"My Sigurd, you are still too young for such a weapon," said his mother. "Wait a few years, and then I will give it to you."

"Give it to me now, I beg you, Mother, for the time has come for me to do the deeds of a hero."

"What are the deeds which you will do, Sigurd?"

"Mother, there is evil which must be conquered,

and there are wrongs which must be made right. I cannot wait!"

"Then come with me, Sigurd, and I will give you the sword." Taking the weapon from the chest in which it lay, she handed it to the eager boy.

When Sigurd saw the sword, he cried out in joy, "Oh, well have you kept it, Mother! Now these pieces shall be welded together, and my father's sword will be mine!"

So once more Sigurd went down to the smithy. "This is the sword which I shall carry with me, Regin," he said. "Mend it for me, as you promised."

Regin took the pieces of the sword and went into the smithy. When he had welded them together, he gave the weapon to the boy, saying, "This sword will never fail you."

Sigurd took the sword in his hand, and lifting it high in the air, brought it down upon the anvil with all his strength. The sword cut through the anvil and did not break. Then Sigurd laughed aloud in his joy, for he knew that he had the strongest sword in the world.

The next day Sigurd went to King Alf and told him that he was about to start on a journey. "I go to slay a cruel dragon and to gain the treasure which he guards," said Sigurd. "The monster is fierce and has killed many people. No one can pass through the land in which he lives."

"Then go, Sigurd," said the king. "Do not be afraid, for you have great strength, and I know that you will win the victory."

SIGURD KILLS THE DRAGON

Early in the morning Sigurd mounted his horse and set out on the road which Regin told him he must take. Out over the plains he rode, and then up a mountain path. On and on he went, until the sun sank from sight, and darkness came on. Then he lay down to rest, and his beautiful horse stood near him.

With the first light of dawn, the young man rose and went on his way. Suddenly he came out from the mountains into a great, high plain. Then he knew that he would soon meet the monster he had come to fight.

Joyously he leaped down from his horse and went forward on foot, looking about for some sign of the dragon. Soon he found a track, which he followed until he came to the edge of a cliff. Far below he saw a beautiful lake.

Then Sigurd knew that this must be the path used by the dragon when he went to drink. As he was thinking how large the dragon must be to leave such a trail, he heard a roar, and the earth seemed to shake under him. The dragon was coming!

The mouth of the monster was open wide, and flames and smoke shot out, so that the sky was darkened. But Sigurd stood still, holding his father's sword until the dragon was close upon him. Then he struck as he had struck upon the anvil, and the dragon fell dead.

SIGURD, THE YOUNG WARRIOR

SIGURD SAVES THE PRINCESS

As Sigurd stood looking down at the body of the monster, a strange and beautiful thing happened. He heard the birds singing in the trees, and suddenly he found that he could understand their language.

One said, "Sigurd has killed the terrible dragon. He will have great praise for this deed."

Another said, "The treasure-house is full of gold. Sigurd may now take it for his own."

The third said, "The gold will not bring happiness to him. But Sigurd should wear the helmet and armor which are with the gold."

The fourth said, "A beautiful princess lies asleep in a castle. She will not awake until Sigurd comes."

The fifth said, "If Sigurd wishes to save the princess, he must go through the wall of fire."

Then Sigurd thought, "I will get the helmet and the armor, and I will save the princess." So he followed the track of the dragon, and it led him to the treasure-house. There he saw great heaps of gold. Sigurd found there, too, the helmet and the armor which the bird had said he would find. He put them on, for he thought he might need them when he came to pass through the wall of fire. Then he set out to find the sleeping princess.

"How shall I find the castle of the princess?" thought Sigurd. But he was not afraid, for his victory over the dragon had made him even more brave. So he rode on and on, until suddenly he saw a light in the distance.

"What can that be?" said Sigurd to himself. "Is it a fire on some distant mountain peak?"

Then he remembered the words which the bird had said: "If Sigurd wishes to save the princess, he must go through the wall of fire."

"Now surely I am on the right path," thought the young hero. "The light which I see must be the fire around the castle."

Sigurd went joyously forward until night came on; then he stopped and lay down to rest. He was so eager to ride on and to find the princess that he could hardly wait for morning. As soon as the sun had risen, he sprang upon his good horse, and they hastened on their way again.

Many hours they traveled. The light grew brighter and brighter until Sigurd could see that it was high on a mountain. Then he knew that he was coming very near to the castle in which lay the sleeping princess. Suddenly he saw the castle; and around it leaped the flames which he had seen so far away.

SIGURD, THE YOUNG WARRIOR

Up the mountain the good horse went. Just before the wall of fire was reached, Sigurd stopped and said to his horse, "In that castle lies a princess whom we must save. If the fire burns us, we shall not turn back, for I must be a hero and must suffer for others, and you are the bravest steed that man ever rode!"

At this the noble horse sprang forward right through the flames to the door of the castle. Then Sigurd leaped from his steed and entered. There was no sign of life as he went from room to room looking for the princess. At last he came to a hall in which someone lay asleep. But the head was covered with a helmet and the body with a war coat, so that Sigurd could not tell who the person might be.

As he gently lifted the helmet, beautiful golden hair fell down over the war coat. Then Sigurd knew that he had found the princess of whom the birds had told him. She lay very still, and her eyes were closed. The young hero knelt down and whispered softly to her, "Princess, awake! I have come to save you!" But the beautiful princess did not stir.

"This heavy armor presses upon her," thought the young warrior. So with the point of his sword he cut the war coat from top to bottom. Still the princess did not wake.

Then he saw that the sleeves of the coat still pressed upon her arms. With his good sword he cut the sleeves open from the shoulder to the hand. As they fell apart, the princess gave a long sigh and turned her head. Slowly she opened her eyes and looked in wonder at Sigurd.

"Who are you who has waked me from my sleep?" she asked.

"I am Sigurd, the son of a great warrior. I killed

the terrible dragon that guarded the treasure, and then I came to save you."

"Who told you that I was here?"

"The birds sang in the trees and told me of you," said the brave young hero.

"How could you come through the fire, Sigurd?"

"There was no other way to reach you, beautiful Princess," he answered.

"Surely you are a great hero, Sigurd. I was told that one who knew not fear should awaken me, and at last you have come!"

"Tell me your name, Princess," said Sigurd.

"My name is Brunhild, and I am the daughter of a great king. Many years have I slept here, because no man dared come through the wall of fire. But you are the bravest of all heroes!"

"And you are the fairest princess in the world, Brunhild!" said the young warrior.

So Sigurd saved the princess, and when people heard what he had done, there was great joy.

As the years went on, Sigurd did many other brave deeds and won many battles, so that his name became known in every land. But wherever the stories of Sigurd's victories were told or sung, people loved best to hear of the killing of the dragon and the saving of Brunhild.

Notes and Questions

1. From pages 276 and 278, choose four words that best tell why Sigurd was truly a hero.

2. (a) Why did Regin want Sigurd to kill the dragon? (b) Why did Sigurd want to kill it?

3. What was it that made Regin's heart bitter and full of hate?

4. From the following list choose three things to show that the Sigurd and Beowulf stories are somewhat alike.

    (a) a beautiful princess   (d) a treasure
    (b) a great blacksmith   (e) a wall of fire
    (c) a magic sword   (f) a terrible monster
       (g) a journey across the sea

5. Below is a list of ten things you can find in the pictures of this story. Write them in a column, and after each one write the page number of the picture that shows it. Some of the things may be in more than one picture. If they are, give the page number of each picture.

    (a) steed   (c) helmet   (e) fire   (g) anvil   (i) armor
    (b) shield (d) spear   (f) sword (h) claws (j) forge

6. Be ready to tell in your own words—
    (a) How Sigurd chose his horse.
    (b) How Sigurd found and killed the dragon.
    (c) How he found and saved the princess.

7. Be ready to read lines that—
    (a) Tell what kind of boy Sigurd was.
    (b) Tell why Sigurd finally agreed to kill the dragon.
    (c) Tell what the birds said.

You can read more about Sigurd in *The Story of Siegfried*, by Baldwin. This book has beautiful pictures drawn by Howard Pyle, a famous American artist.

ROLAND, THE NOBLE KNIGHT

Clara E. Lynch

To the people of France in olden times Roland was the great hero. The story of his brave deeds was sung by minstrels nearly a thousand years ago. Then it was written down in a long poem called "The Song of Roland." A great general once ordered his army to sing a song about Roland as it went to battle so that his soldiers would try to be as brave as the great hero.

ROLAND'S BOYHOOD

There once lived in Italy a woman named Bertha and her little boy, Roland. They were so poor that a cave in the hillside was their only home, and often they did not have enough to eat. But Roland, even when he was hungry, tried to be brave and cheerful for his mother's sake.

No one would have guessed that the little boy in ragged clothes was the nephew of the great king of France, whose name was known all over the world. Roland himself did not know this. His mother never talked to him about her old home in France or about her brother, the great King Charlemagne, or Charles the Great, as he was often called.

Charlemagne had been very angry when his sister Bertha married a man who was not a prince. So Bertha had to leave the palace and go out with her husband to find a new home. They were without money, and no one in France dared to give them shelter. So they wandered far away.

At last, near a small town in Italy, they found a cave in the side of a hill. Here they made their home, and here their little boy grew up. Although they were poor, yet they were very happy, until one day Roland's father was drowned.

Roland was too young to miss his father much, but his mother was very sad. Often when the young boy came in from play, he would find her weeping. "Do not weep, Mother," he would say. "I am here, and I love you."

ROLAND, THE NOBLE KNIGHT 297

All the children of the neighborhood came to the hillside to play with Roland, so that he was never lonely. Among these boys was Oliver, the little son of the governor of the town. Roland and Oliver became great friends, although Oliver lived in a castle and Roland in a cave. Oliver wore velvet and silk, but Roland's suit was made of the roughest cloth and was nearly always ragged. As Roland grew older, he saw that his clothes were not like those of the other boys.

"Mother," he said one day, "I do not like these clothes. The boys call them rags. Why cannot I have a suit such as Oliver wears?"

"Roland, my son," said his mother, sadly, "Oliver's father is governor of the town. Your father is dead, and we are very poor. I cannot always get bread for us to eat."

The boy was silent for a few minutes. He was thinking about what his mother had just told him. Then he spoke again.

"Mother, was your home always in this cave?"

His mother smiled sadly as she said, "Once I lived in a beautiful palace, Roland. But that was in a land far away from here."

"A palace, Mother!" cried the little boy. "Did you live in a palace? Oliver told me once that only kings and very great men live in palaces. Was your father a great man in that beautiful land in which you lived?"

"My father was the king of that land, Roland," said his mother, quietly.

"Then, Mother, you must be a princess! But how can you be a princess without servants or soldiers?" eagerly asked the boy.

"I do not need servants or soldiers. My son's hands will wait upon me and fight for me."

Then the little boy laughed and clapped his hands. "Let us play that this cave is your palace, Mother, and that I am the army guarding it."

Roland never tired of this game, and when the other boys joined him, they would play soldiers, too. With Roland as their captain, the little company would march up and down.

CHARLEMAGNE FINDS ROLAND

During the years that Roland had been playing on the hillside, his uncle, King Charlemagne, had been fighting the enemies of his country. He had won battle after battle, until he had conquered many lands. Now he was known as the greatest warrior in the world.

Then it happened that he went traveling in

ROLAND, THE NOBLE KNIGHT 299

Italy, one of the countries he now ruled over. He stopped at the town near which Bertha was living in a cave. He knew that the people would like to see him, and he thought of a plan to give them pleasure. He ordered great tables to be placed under the trees and spread with rich food. When he and his nobles sat down to dinner, crowds of people stood around to look at the great king. Many of them were poor and hungry, and Charlemagne ordered his servants to give them bread and meat from the tables.

That morning neither Roland nor his mother had had any breakfast; so the little boy went out to see if he could find any wild fruit to take home. Seeing a crowd of people hurrying along, he followed them.

When Roland saw the tables spread with food, and servants handing bread and meat to the people, he was so surprised that he could not move. It was a wonderful sight for a hungry boy. "And all this is to be given away!" he thought. "Now Mother will have a good dinner!"

He did not wait for anyone to give him the food, but walked straight to a table and gathered up as much as he could hold in his arms. Everyone looked in surprise at the beautiful boy in the strange clothes, who fearlessly took bread and meat from the king's own table.

Although Roland saw nothing but the food, the watchful eyes of the great king had seen everything. His servants would have seized the boy, but Charlemagne said, "Do not touch him. Tomorrow we shall dine here again. If the boy returns, bring him to me."

Roland hurried joyously to his mother with the food. The next day he came again just as the king seated himself at the table. A crowd of poor people stood around, waiting to receive bread and meat. Roland again walked to the table and gathered up as much food as he could carry.

Before he could turn away, however, a voice said, "Come here, my boy."

A servant led Roland to the head of the table, and the little boy with his arms full of food stood before the great king. Charlemagne looked kindly at him and said, "If you are hungry, my child, sit down and eat as much as you want."

"You are very good," said Roland, "but I cannot wait. I must take this food home at once to my mother."

The great king smiled as he heard these words. "Who is your mother?" he asked.

"My mother is a princess," answered Roland.

Some of the people standing around laughed when they heard this answer from the poorly dressed boy. But Charlemagne did not laugh, for Roland looked so straight and so fearlessly into his eyes that the king was sure the boy spoke the truth.

"Where is your mother's castle?" he asked.

"On the hillside not far from here," said Roland.

"Has your mother, the princess, servants to wait upon her, and soldiers to fight for her?" asked Charlemagne.

"My hands wait upon her, and my hands will fight for her," answered Roland.

The king laughed and told the child to run home to his mother. Then Charlemagne rose from the table and followed Roland to his home. The king saw the boy enter the cave and heard his happy voice as he showed his mother the food he had brought.

When Charlemagne started to follow Roland into the cave, Bertha looked up and saw him in the doorway. With a cry, "Charles, my brother!" she ran toward him. But suddenly she stopped, and would have fallen if the king had not caught her.

As soon as she could speak, she told Roland that this was his uncle Charles, whom he had never seen. But when Roland looked into Charlemagne's face, he knew that it was a face he had seen before. This was the man who had sat at the head of the great table.

ROLAND'S NEW HOME

Soon Roland was telling his uncle how he loved to play soldier on the hillside.

"Will you come to live with me, Roland, and learn to be a real soldier?" asked the king.

"Will Mother come, too?" asked Roland anxiously.

"Yes, your mother will come, too, and we shall all live together in a great palace and be very happy."

"May I take Oliver with me?" asked the little boy eagerly.

"We cannot take him with us, Roland," said Charlemagne, after Bertha had told him what great friends the two boys were. "But perhaps Oliver's father will bring him to see you some time."

This comforted Roland a little, and when his uncle told him that he would have a horse to ride and a little sword of his own, he was very happy. So when Charlemagne returned to France, Roland and his mother went with him to live in the palace.

As the years passed, the boy grew tall and strong, and he learned to use the sword and the lance. He hoped some day to be as brave a soldier as his uncle, and often begged the king to let him go with the army.

At last Roland was old enough to ride out with the knights who followed Charlemagne. In his first battle the young hero saved his uncle's life. After that whenever King Charles went to war, Roland went with him. Soon he became known over all the world for his great deeds. The king was proud of his brave nephew, and the soldiers would follow wherever he led.

But Roland never boasted of his great deeds. "It was nothing," he would say when people praised him. Then he would tell of brave battles fought by others and would say how proud he was of his comrades. Sometimes, when he was starting out to war, he would look around him at the brave knights and say, "Oh, if Oliver were only here, how happy I should be!"

CHARLEMAGNE AND ROLAND IN SPAIN

About this time Charlemagne heard that a terrible people from Spain, called Saracens, had entered France. He prepared to fight them, and from all the country, warriors came to join his army. To Roland's great joy, Oliver was one of these knights, and from that time the two friends were always together.

For seven years the war went on, until at last the Saracens left France and returned to Spain. But Charlemagne knew that his country would never be safe until his enemies had been conquered. So he followed them into Spain and drove them out of every city except one. Then the Saracen king, Marsilius, thought of a plan to deceive Charlemagne and make him return to France.

One day as the great Charles was resting in the shade of a beautiful tree, Saracen messengers came and knelt down before him.

"O great Charles," said the leader, "we come to you from Marsilius. He sends you rich presents and begs you to return to France. He promises that he will follow you there in one month, and that he will never fight you again."

Charlemagne sat silent for some moments. Then he called his warriors around him and said: "King Marsilius has sent messengers to me, bringing rich gifts and asking me to return to France. He promises to follow me there and never more fight against me. Tell me what answer I should send him."

As soon as Charlemagne had finished speaking, Roland exclaimed, "My advice is, fight on! France will never be safe until Marsilius is conquered."

The great king bent his head, but did not answer. Then a knight named Ganelon rose and stood before him. "Roland is young and talks foolishly," he said. "Listen not to him. Let us accept the offer of King Marsilius and end this long war, so that we may return to our homes."

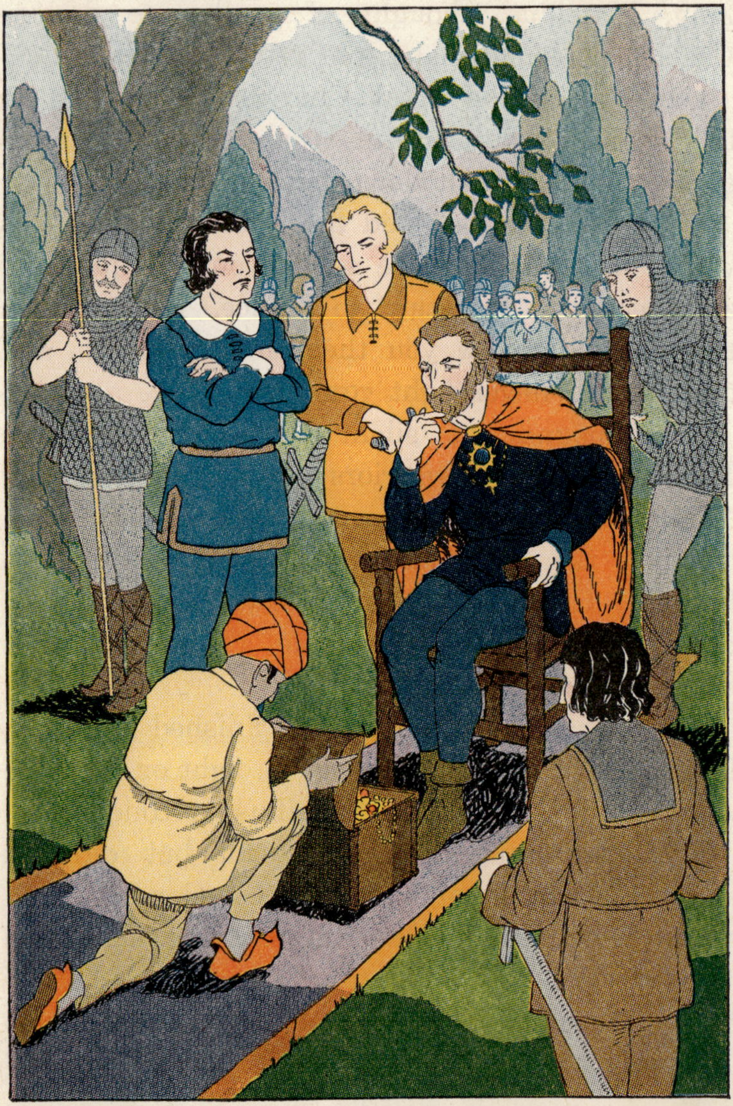

Then all the knights cried out together, "Ganelon has spoken wisely! Let us end this war!"

"Tell me, then, whom shall I send to carry my message to King Marsilius?" asked Charlemagne.

"Let me be your messenger," said Roland.

"You must not go," cried Oliver. "The Saracens may put you to death. I will go."

"Neither of you shall go!" cried Charlemagne. "You are both too young."

At this there was silence; then Roland spoke again. "Let Ganelon go. He is wise, and he will do the errand well."

At this all the knights cried out, "Roland is right! Let Ganelon go! Let Ganelon carry the king's message!"

GANELON'S WICKED PLAN

Charlemagne ordered Ganelon to go at once to King Marsilius. Now Ganelon did not want to carry the message, for Marsilius had once put to death a messenger who had been sent to him by Charlemagne.

So Ganelon was very angry, and he thought, "Roland is to blame for this! I shall always hate him and Oliver, his friend, for they have planned this thing!" Then the angry knight turned to Roland and said, "If ever I return, I will make you suffer for this!"

"I do not fear you, Ganelon," said Roland. "But I will gladly go instead of you, if the king will let me carry the message."

Ganelon took Charlemagne's letter and set out. On his way, he caught up with the Saracen messengers, who were returning to Marsilius. Their leader began to talk to him about Charlemagne and his victories.

"This Charles is a wonderful man," he said. "He has fought many great battles and conquered many lands. Why does he not now give up war and spend the rest of his days in peace?"

"Roland is the one to blame," answered Ganelon. "He wishes his uncle to conquer the whole world. There will never be peace while Roland lives. But if Roland should die, Charles would return home and fight no more."

"Tell me how we may kill this Roland," said the Saracen, for he saw that Ganelon hated the brave young prince.

"I know how Roland may surely be put to death, but I will tell my plan only to King Marsilius himself," said Ganelon.

When they reached the Saracens' camp, Ganelon

was led to the king, who said to him, "Much do I wonder at this Charles. Will he never grow tired of war?"

"Never while Roland lives," answered Ganelon. "Charles is not afraid of any man while he has Roland and Oliver with him."

"Tell me how I may kill this Roland, for men say he is so strong and brave that a thousand men cannot stand against him."

Then Ganelon told his wicked plan. "Send even richer gifts to King Charles and promise again that you will never more fight against him. He will believe you, and he will return to France at once. But a guard will be left in the mountains until the great army has crossed over. In this guard will be Roland and Oliver and many other brave knights of France.

"When the rest of the army has passed over the mountains, send one hundred thousand men against this guard. Your men will all be killed, for Roland's soldiers will fight like lions. Then send another hundred thousand against them, when they are weak and weary from the struggle of the first battle. By this plan Roland and Oliver will surely be killed, and Charles will never go to war again."

"Your plan is good," said the king. "But how can I be sure that Roland will stay in the mountains with the guard?"

"Roland will always be where the greatest danger is," answered Ganelon. "When Charles goes to battle, Roland is always in the lead. But when the army leaves Spain, the danger will be from behind. Roland will stay until the last soldier has passed over the mountains."

Marsilius was so pleased with Ganelon's plan that he gave him rich presents. Then seven hundred camels, loaded with gold and silver, were sent as a gift to Charlemagne.

Mounting his horse, Ganelon started back to his own camp. The great Charles was glad to see him and asked what message he brought from Marsilius.

"Marsilius has sent you seven hundred camels loaded with gold and silver, and he will follow you to France before a month has passed. He will never again fight against you, but will always obey you."

This message pleased the king, and he praised Ganelon. Then a thousand trumpets were sounded, and Charlemagne's great army made ready for the journey to France.

ROLAND'S DANGEROUS TASK

When all was ready, Charlemagne said to his knights: "The mountain pass through which we must go is narrow. If the enemy should attack us there, we could neither fight nor escape. Who will stay behind and keep the enemy back until our army has gone through the pass?"

"You have no braver knight than Roland," said Ganelon. "Give him command of the guard."

Now Charlemagne did not want to leave Roland behind, but Roland smiled and said, "Gladly will I do this. I thank Ganelon for naming me." Charlemagne bowed his head, for he feared that some harm might come to Roland.

Then Oliver came quickly to Roland's side. "If my comrade stays behind, I will stay with him," he said.

"And I," cried one after another of the men, until the whole army would have remained with Roland; but he would allow only twenty thousand soldiers to stay.

Then the rest of the great army started on the journey to France. The soldiers had been away seven years and were happy to think that they would soon be home again. But as they marched along, Charlemagne became very sad.

"I am leaving Roland in a strange land among his enemies," he said. "If he is killed, I shall never be happy again."

When the soldiers saw their king so sorrowful, they feared that they would never see Roland again. Gladly would they have turned back to save him.

Now Roland needed their help, for as Charlemagne marched away from Spain, a great Saracen army was coming into the narrow pass in the mountains. Suddenly a thousand trumpets were blown, and the sound reached the ears of the soldiers on guard.

"Listen!" said Oliver. "Do you hear the sound of trumpets?"

"The Saracens are coming!" cried Roland.

Then Oliver climbed a mountain peak and saw the great Saracen army moving forward. Hastening to Roland, he cried, "I have seen one hundred thousand Saracens coming toward us. We shall have a terrible battle!"

Roland then spoke to his soldiers, telling them that a great army of the enemy was close upon them. "We trusted Marsilius, and he has deceived us," he said. "But we can show the Saracens how brave men die."

ROLAND, THE NOBLE KNIGHT 313

ROLAND'S LAST BATTLE

The Saracens came on, feeling sure of victory because of their great numbers. But the soldiers led by Roland and Oliver fought so bravely that at last the enemy fled. Then Roland went over the battlefield, mourning for the many noble knights who had fallen in that fierce battle.

Suddenly he heard the sound of trumpets again, and he knew that another army of the enemy was coming against them. "Oliver," he said, "surely Ganelon planned this attack. He wishes to have us killed. We cannot now hope for victory, but let us die bravely."

On came the Saracens, but when they attacked Roland's army, they were driven back again and again. At last so many Saracens had fallen that those who were left fled from the field.

In these two battles many of the guard had been killed. Roland wept for the brave soldiers who would never again follow him to battle, and Oliver cried, "Oh, if King Charles had only been here!"

Then for the third time trumpets rang out, and over the mountains came another great Saracen army. Once again Roland's weary soldiers got ready for battle. Four times they drove back the enemy, but at last they could do no more. One by one the knights had fallen until only a few were left.

Roland looked around at the brave men fighting against such great numbers, and he thought that perhaps even yet some of them could be saved. So he raised his horn to his lips and blew with all his strength.

Far away on the other side of the mountains, Charlemagne heard that sound. "I hear Roland's horn," he cried. "Roland calls to me for help! I must go to him." Then the king with his great army turned back to help the guard.

While Charlemagne and his army were hastening back over the mountains, the soldiers of the guard were fighting bravely. At last a coward struck Oliver from behind with his spear. Then Oliver called Roland to him, for he knew that he was dying. Roland ran quickly to his comrade and put his arms about the wounded warrior. "O Oliver, my friend, how can I live without you!" he cried.

Oliver spoke loving words to Roland; then his head dropped on Roland's shoulder, and the brave knight died.

For hours the battle went on. At last Roland alone was left to fight the enemy. But not one of the Saracens dared to come within reach of his sword. Suddenly, as they circled around him, fearing to come near, they heard the trumpets of Charlemagne.

"The trumpets of France," they cried. "The great Charles is coming. We must escape while there is yet time!"

So four hundred of the bravest Saracens went as near to Roland as they dared and threw their spears at him. Then they fled from the field.

Again the trumpets rang out, and this time the sound was near at hand. But Roland knew that Charlemagne's army had come too late. Oliver was dead, and so were all the other faithful friends who had followed him to battle. Roland himself was so badly wounded that he knew he could not live.

He climbed a little hill and lay down under a pine tree with his face toward the land of Spain, closing his eyes as if to sleep. When Charlemagne and his army came, they found him lying there, and they knew that France had lost her greatest warrior and her noblest knight.

ROLAND, THE NOBLE KNIGHT

Notes and Questions

1. Name these people who took part in this story:
    - (a) a brother and a sister
    - (b) two good friends
    - (c) uncle and nephew
    - (d) the king of the Saracens
    - (e) a knight who was untrue to his country
    - (f) Roland's best friend

2. (a) Which two people in the story did you like best? (b) Which did you dislike?

3. Here are five things that happened in this story. Choose the two most important.
    - (a) Roland finds Oliver again.
    - (b) The Saracen messengers come.
    - (c) Charlemagne finds the boy Roland.
    - (d) Ganelon carries the message.
    - (e) Roland stays with the rear guard.

4. Why was Ganelon angry at being sent as a messenger to the Saracens?

5. Choose the best ending to the sentence below. Ganelon deceived Charlemagne because
    - (a) he was disloyal to his country.
    - (b) he loved riches.
    - (c) he hated Roland.

6. Be ready to read lines that tell about the pictures on pages 300 and 306.

7. On page 310 find lines that tell why Roland was sure to be left to guard the army.

8. Be ready to tell in your own words—
    - (a) How Charlemagne happened to find Roland.
    - (b) How Ganelon planned with the Saracens to bring about Roland's death.

You would enjoy reading "Roland and Oliver," Green and Kirk (in *With Spurs of Gold*).

A BACKWARD LOOK

Hundreds of years have gone by since the time of Beowulf, Sigurd, and Roland. Yet people love to read of these great heroes. Why has their fame lasted through all these years? Thousands of men, whose names have long since been forgotten, were as brave as they. If you read thoughtfully, you know why these heroes have not been forgotten. You saw that they were not only brave; they were truthful, unselfish, and loyal to their friends. They faced danger in order to help their fellow-men.

As you read these stories, perhaps you felt that you, too, would like to win fame and honor when you grow older. Of course you cannot battle savage monsters and slay fierce dragons, but there is work to be done in this world that calls for unselfish and brave men and women.

Only a few years ago, a brave American doctor went to a country where the dreaded yellow fever killed more people each year than ever did Grendel in the days of Beowulf. Risking his life as he studied the disease, at last he learned the secret of how people became ill with it, and he rid the country of its terrible enemy. Was not he as great a hero as even Beowulf?

After all, to be the noblest kind of hero means only to be a helper of our fellow-men, to be a *good citizen* of our country. Now try making your play.

PART · VII

HOLIDAYS AND FESTIVALS

CHRISTMAS IN THE HEART

It is Christmas in the mansion,
   Yule-log fires and silken frocks.
It is Christmas in the cottage,
   Mother's filling little socks.
It is Christmas on the highway
   In the thronging, busy mart;
But the dearest, truest Christmas
   Is the Christmas in the heart.

HOLIDAYS ARE REMEMBERING DAYS

Holidays are happy days for all of us. When we speak of them, we think of turkey dinners, parades and bands, picnics and presents. Often on holidays we go to visit our friends and relatives, or they come to spend a few days with us.

But did you ever stop to think that most holidays are "remembering days" as well as happy days? In our own lives and in the life of our country, important things have happened that we do not want to forget. Fourth of July reminds us every year of the long and brave struggle our country went through to win its freedom. On Washington's Birthday we think of that great American, our first President, who so wisely and unselfishly led our people in their fight for liberty.

So with Thanksgiving Day, Mother's Day, Christmas, and Memorial Day—they all are set apart so that we may not forget the good things that have come to us, and the brave, unselfish men and women who have done so much to make our country and the world a happier place in which to live.

In this, the last Part of your book, you will read stories and poems that tell of some holidays that we so much enjoy. As you read, try to see how each story and poem tells the true meaning of the holiday.

HALLOWEEN

Nancy Byrd Turner

When pumpkins shine like balls of gold,
   And the moon hangs big and mellow;
When the black cat's fur is thick and cold
   And the gray cat's eyes are yellow;
When nuts fall plunk, and the frost cuts keen—
   Look out, it's Halloween!

Now keep your eye on the tallest broom;
   For if not, woe betide it—
An imp will whisk it out of the room,
   And a gay old witch will ride it.
Never again will that broom be seen—
   So watch out, Halloween!

REMEMBERING DAY

Mary Wight Saunders

All the soldiers marching along;
All the children singing a song;
All the flowers dewy and sweet,
All the flags hung out in the street;
Hearts that throb in a grateful way—
For this is our Remembering Day.

THE FIRST THANKSGIVING DAY

Over three hundred years ago the ship *Mayflower* sailed into Massachusetts Bay. On board were the Pilgrims, who had come from England to make homes in the New World. They landed in the middle of the winter, and before spring most of them died of hunger and cold. Now summer had passed, their crops had grown well, and there would be food for all. So they gathered to give thanks that they were alive and that there was food.

Time—November, 1621
Scene—A Log House in Plymouth Colony

Persons:

FATHER AND MOTHER
BETTY ⎫
EDWARD ⎬ Their Children
RICHARD ⎭
AUNT RUTH
MILES STANDISH
PRISCILLA MULLENS
JOHN ALDEN
MARY ⎫
ROBERT ⎬ Orphans
SQUANTO and Other Indians

[An iron pot hangs over an open fire; in it a porridge is steaming. Betty and Edward sit on the fireplace seat. The mother spins, Aunt Ruth knits, and Mary sews.]

MOTHER. Turn that largest log, Edward. We must have a bright fire for Father's return. Robert and Richard will soon be here, too.

BETTY. Where are they, Mother?

MOTHER. Father is at the town-meeting. Richard and Robert are helping Isaac Allerton to build his house.

AUNT RUTH. [*Looking up from her knitting.*] Hard work seems to agree with the lads. They are doing well, too. They have helped in the building of nearly every house in the village. They will be grown men before we know it.

MOTHER. Stir the porridge, Betty. Our builders will be hungry, and supper must not be late.

THE FIRST THANKSGIVING DAY 325

Mary. You are always kind and thoughtful. I shall never forget your goodness to me since my dear father and mother died in the terrible days of the great sickness. [*She bows her head and weeps gently.*]

Mother. [*Cheerfully.*] Wipe away those tears, Mary, and let us think of the many things we can still be thankful for. The best cure for sorrow is work, and you have had plenty of work here. You have been a great help to us. I am glad that you were sent here when the homeless children were divided among us.

Betty. I am glad, too, that you live with us, Mary. You teach me so many useful things. May I get my sampler and work on it now, Mother, while you spin? Will you show me what stitches to take next?

Mother. Not for a little while, Betty. Just now you must watch the porridge, and stir it when necessary.

Edward. [*Eagerly.*] I hear steps, Mother!

Mother. It must be your father. Run quickly, Betty, and open the door. Stir that log, Edward.

Betty. [*Looking out of window.*] It is Father, and John Alden is with him.

Father and John Alden enter.

FATHER. Come in, John, and sit by our fire for a while. The good wife will be glad to have a chat with you before you go on your way.

JOHN ALDEN. [*Nodding to all.*] Good day to you. How warm and comfortable you are here!

MOTHER. Yes, things are much better with Plymouth Colony than they were a year ago.

MARY. Oh, that terrible winter! I can never forget it.

MOTHER. It is better to think of the good we have than to be unhappy over what we cannot change.

FATHER. We have much to be thankful for. Less than a year ago we had nothing to eat except our small supply of Indian corn, and were afraid that even that would soon be gone.

JOHN ALDEN. Well do I remember the day when our share was but five kernels of corn each. Now we have food in plenty. [*He goes to the fire and warms his hands.*]

AUNT RUTH. How thankful we should be that our lives were spared in that dreadful time, and that our harvest has been so large.

FATHER. That is what Governor Bradford said today in the town-meeting, and so he has set a day for public thanksgiving. First we are to

THE FIRST THANKSGIVING DAY 327

gather at the meeting-house for prayer and praise. Then there is to be a great feast. For three days we are to make merry.

MOTHER. Governor Bradford sets us all a good example. None of us can forget that sad day, before we had left the *Mayflower,* when he came back to the ship to find his wife dead by drowning. Yet no one ever saw him give way to his sorrow.

JOHN ALDEN. And in the time of the great sickness he and our good captain, Miles Standish, never grew tired of caring for the sick and dying.

MARY. It seems hard that our brave Captain's love and care could not save the life of sweet Rose Standish.

MOTHER. When we bear our sorrows bravely, it makes our hearts tender. Miles Standish is a rough soldier, but no one in the world has a kinder heart.

EDWARD. [*Suddenly interrupting.*] Oh, Father! please tell us about the feast. Are the children to go?

FATHER. Everyone is to go. Even the Indians are to be invited. They will learn that we are truly their friends, and that we wish to share our good things with them.

EDWARD. [*Getting up and going to Father.*] But the feast, Father! Do tell us about the feast!

FATHER. In a moment you shall hear about the feast, but a thankful heart is better than a feast. Do not forget to give thanks in your heart for the peace and plenty that we now have.

BETTY. Oh, but we do give thanks, Father! Every day of our lives we are glad that we are no longer hungry.

MARY. And we give thanks that Squanto is our friend and helps us to be friendly with the other Indians.

BETTY. They look so fierce and so strong, Father, and there are so many of them! Every night when I climb up to our dark loft to sleep I am glad that we do not need to fear the Indians any longer.

EDWARD. [*Going to Betty and speaking proudly.*] When I am a man, Betty, I will be a soldier like Captain Miles Standish. I will carry a gun and a sword. Then you will never need to fear the Indians.

FATHER. Let us hope that Massasoit and his men may keep the peace with us so well that there will be no need for guns and swords when you are a man, Edward.

THE FIRST THANKSGIVING DAY

MOTHER. Squanto is a true friend to us. He has been a great help in this new home of ours. He will do all he can in helping us to keep peace with Massasoit.

JOHN ALDEN. He has taught us many things. We knew nothing about corn until he taught us to plant it in the hills.

FATHER. And to hoe the earth around the stalks, if we wished to have fat ears of corn.

EDWARD. Squanto taught Robert and Richard how to catch eels. They go down to the shore and stamp them out of the mud with their feet. Sometimes the mud is full of fat eels. Oh, I wish that I were as big as Richard. Then I would tread out eels! [*In his excitement he stamps his feet as though he were treading out eels.*]

MOTHER. Often we would have gone hungry, if it had not been for a pot of good eel broth.

AUNT RUTH. Squanto showed the lads where to find lobsters, too, and how to catch them.

MARY. And he taught us how to pound the corn into meal, and how to cook the meal.

BETTY. [*Leaving the kettle and going to Mother.*] Mother, will you teach me how to make a journey-cake from pounded meal?

MOTHER. Yes, Betty, but do not forget to stir the

meal in the kettle, or we may have scorched porridge before we have a journey-cake.

[Betty goes back hastily to the fire-seat and again stirs the porridge. At this moment laughter and boyish voices are heard outside. The door suddenly opens, and the two lads, Robert and Richard, enter.]

AUNT RUTH. Here are our builders. How did the building of Isaac Allerton's house go on today?

ROBERT. It is almost finished. There were five of us at work on it this afternoon.

FATHER. You have done well. This is the seventh house in Plymouth; with the meeting-house and the store-houses it makes a year's work that our builders may be proud of. [*A knock on the door is heard.*] Hurry and open the door, Richard.

Priscilla Mullens enters.

MOTHER. Good day, Priscilla. How is it that you are out at this time of day? You are always so busy when it nears the time for the evening meal. [*Gives Priscilla a chair near the fire.*]

PRISCILLA. It is the news of the great feast that has brought me here when I should be at the fireside stirring porridge, like Betty. I came to see if you can spare Mary to help me tomorrow.

THE FIRST THANKSGIVING DAY

Do you know that Massasoit and his ninety men are to be here for three days? Is not that a great number for the four busy wives of Plymouth to feed?

MOTHER. It is true, Priscilla, that the great sickness left but four wives in Plymouth, but the maidens are strong and willing. You are but a maiden, Priscilla, but you have a woman's heart. When I see you so cheerful and so busy day after day, you seem to me to have the strength of ten women.

AUNT RUTH. We must all work to prepare for the feast. It is good that we have such a large supply of plums and grapes.

MOTHER. This feast will not be like our English feasts. We cannot make the old dainties. We have neither milk nor eggs. We have no good beef and mutton, and no flour to make fine bread.

FATHER. [*Cheerily.*] We must not wish for these things, wife. We have found a land of liberty. We will take what it can give us and be thankful.

MOTHER. I know; I know! We will do our best.

AUNT RUTH. We have plenty of corn for porridge and hominy and Betty's journey-cakes.

PRISCILLA. I have been trying my hand at these

great golden pumpkins. They make fine pie. I want Mary to help me make many of them.

AUNT RUTH. [*Moving her chair nearer to Priscilla.*] We have heard of your pumpkin pies. Every cook in Plymouth wants to try making them. There must be many pumpkin pies for the Governor's Thanksgiving feast.

PRISCILLA. Tomorrow we must get up early. The days will not be long enough for all we have to do.

MOTHER. And night is a poor time to work, when our only light is firelight and a fish-oil lamp.

MARY. I wish we had the tallow candles of England.

FATHER. Have patience. In good time we shall be able to send to England a shipload of things we have raised in this new land. Then we will ask for cows in return, and we shall no longer be without the milk and butter and cheese, and the beef and tallow, of our English home.

JOHN ALDEN. Governor Bradford says that now the harvest is over we must get together a fine load of beaver-fur and sassafras to send back on the next ship that comes to Plymouth.

PRISCILLA. [*Arising.*] I must go now, to prepare supper for our household.

JOHN ALDEN. [*Hastily arising.*] I will walk home with you, Priscilla, if I may.

Priscilla and John Alden go out.

EDWARD. [*Going over to his mother.*] Since Priscilla and Mary are to make so many pumpkin pies for the feast, may I have two pieces, Mother?

MOTHER. He who eats must first earn. What can you do for the great feast, Edward?

EDWARD. Oh, I had not thought of that! Let me see! I can bring wood for the fire and carry water.

BETTY. And I can shine the pewter platters.

FATHER. There are lobsters and fish in the ocean, and eels on the shore. There are turkeys and deer and bear in the forest. It may be that your mother will not miss the English dainties, after all.

EDWARD. [*Going excitedly to his father.*] Oh, Father! Are you going to hunt for turkeys? May I go with you? Do you think that I can shoot a bear? Or maybe a deer? Then Betty can have a deer-skin dress such as Squanto says the Indian maids wear.

ROBERT. Squanto says that the bears are very

fierce, and that the deer are so swift that they can run away much faster than a small boy with a heavy gun can follow.

FATHER. Do not try for bear, Edward, until you have learned to shoot, or we may have a sad Thanksgiving day.

[The sound of footsteps is heard. Robert runs to the window and looks out. Seeing Captain Miles Standish, he throws the door wide open. Standish, with gun on shoulder, enters.]

MILES STANDISH. Good day to you all! Who of you would like to go for a hunt tomorrow? We shall need many turkeys to feed Massasoit and his ninety men.

FATHER. Welcome, Captain! There are three here to join you, for Richard shall go with us tomorrow, on his first hunt.

RICHARD. How glad I am, Father, that you will let me go! Squanto says the turkeys are very plentiful this year, and big and fat.

MILES STANDISH. After the hunt we will practice shooting. Then at the feast we can show the Indians how well we can defend ourselves.

FATHER. [*Hearing footsteps.*] Go to the door, Richard, and see who are outside.

[Richard goes outside and in a moment returns with Squanto and three other Indians.]

335

RICHARD. Father, here are Squanto and three other Indians. They wish to tell Captain Standish that they are on their way to Massasoit's camp.

MILES STANDISH. [*Going up to Squanto.*] Welcome, Squanto. What is it you wish?

SQUANTO. The white men make a great feast. Squanto goes to tell Massasoit to bring all his men.

MILES STANDISH. Tell Massasoit that the Governor wishes him and his men to stay with us for three days. We will do our best to feast them well.

SQUANTO. Squanto will tell Massasoit. But first Massasoit will go on a great hunt. He will bring many deer for the feast.

Squanto and other Indians go out.

MILES STANDISH. Right glad will we be if Massasoit and his men bring some deer for the feast. Ninety Indians will be a goodly number to feed. Good night.

Miles Standish, gun on his shoulder, goes out.

FATHER. Let us get to our supper and then to bed. We have busy days before us. And I hope that, as we prepare for our feast, Edward and Betty will not think more of the good things to eat

THE FIRST THANKSGIVING DAY

than of the goodness of God in guiding us to this free land.

MOTHER. And give thanks, too, that we are all here together, well and strong and ready to be joyful on our first THANKSGIVING DAY.

NOTES AND QUESTIONS

1. Tell three reasons why the Pilgrims were thankful. Perhaps you can tell more than three.

2. (a) How many days did the first Thanksgiving last?
   (b) What did the Pilgrims do first on Thanksgiving?
   (c) How did the Indians help?

3. Name two very important people in the colony and tell why each was important.

4. Name five ways in which Squanto helped the white people.

5. From this list choose the things that the Pilgrims had: stoves, candles, wheat flour, milk, cornmeal, eggs, butter, pumpkins, fish.

6. Find and be ready to read lines that tell—
   (a) How the Pilgrims had suffered from hunger.
   (b) Why the Pilgrims loved Governor Bradford and Miles Standish.
   (c) What buildings there were in Plymouth.
   (d) How the Pilgrims hoped to be able to get things from England.

Other Thanksgiving stories are "Grandma's Thanksgiving Story," Lotherington (in *Child-Library Readers, Book Three*); "An Old Time Thanksgiving," Talbot (in *Indian Stories Retold from St. Nicholas*). You would enjoy, also, *Stories of the Pilgrims,* Pumphrey.

A SURPRISE CHRISTMAS

Marian Willard

This story is called "A Surprise Christmas," but perhaps just as good a name would be "The Animals' Santa Claus." As you read, see whether you think so, too.

WHY BETTY AND BOB WERE UNHAPPY

It was Christmas morning—the day when Bob and Betty should have been having the merriest time in the world. But they were not merry at all; they sat and looked at each other and hardly knew whether to laugh or to cry.

"That letter is the best present we could have had, anyway," said Betty as she looked again at the big special-delivery stamp. "Mother is now out of danger, and we will be home in a few weeks."

When Mother had become sick, just after Thanksgiving, the children had been sent to Uncle Ben's farm. They had played in the meadows, gone to school in the little schoolhouse, and watched for the postman to bring letters from home.

Christmas at home meant days of shopping, fun with Uncle Tom when he came back from college, parties at the church and at the schoolhouse. Besides, Christmas at home meant planning a gift for some little child that was poor.

A SURPRISE CHRISTMAS

"I wish we could have some kind of Christmas this year," said Bob, "just to keep us from forgetting what day it is. There isn't even snow," and he looked at the bare, brown fields. "At home they've all been so worried about Mother that probably no one has had time to buy us any presents."

"Well, Bobby, Mother is better, and that is the best present in all the world for us," and Betty smiled bravely at her brother.

"I wish we could make a Christmas for somebody else," said Bobby slowly. "But there aren't any poor people up here. Besides, we couldn't buy anything, for there aren't any stores. Isn't this the strangest Christmas you ever saw?"

"Yes, Bob, it is. No place to spend money; woods full of Christmas trees and no presents to put on them; no one who needs help; no snow, no skating, no company. We are going to have a good Christmas dinner, though—a pair of big chickens."

"And I'm going to crack some butternuts right now," said Bobby, and he jumped up and left his sister to romp with Shep, the collie.

"Oh, Shep, Shep, I'll give *you* a Christmas present," and Betty ran upstairs and came flying down again with a big blue ribbon in her hand.

"There, old fellow," she said as she tied a bow on Shep's collar, "you have a Christmas present."

Then she clapped her hands and ran for Bobby. "Oh, Bob, hurry up and finish your butternuts. I think we can have a Christmas after all. Hurry!"

BETTY PLANS A SURPRISE

Betty ran to find Uncle Ben and whisper something in his ear. Then she began to do the queerest things. Up to the attic she ran and down again, her arms full of boxes and bundles; then down to the cellar, and up with an armful of carrots and apples; then out to the barn and back.

A SURPRISE CHRISTMAS 341

By that time Bobby had cracked all the butternuts for dinner and stood with his hands in his pockets, watching his sister. "What in the world are you going to do?" he asked with a grin.

Betty grinned back at him. "You take the ax and go over to the grove and cut down a Christmas tree. Uncle Ben said we could have one."

"But we haven't a thing to put on it."

"We shall have something when you get back. Uncle Ben will go with the horse and wagon and bring the tree home."

Bob went off, wondering, and Betty began to cut out pieces from an old gray flannel shirt of Uncle Ben's and to hunt in the button box for old shoe buttons.

When Bob drove in with Uncle Ben and the little tree, Betty dangled in front of her brother seven gray mice by their tails of string. With shoe buttons for eyes and bodies made of gray flannel, they looked so real that Uncle Ben jumped when he saw them.

"My land, child, those mice would fool any cat in the country!"

"Smell," answered Betty, as she dangled them under her uncle's nose.

"Catnip mice," he chuckled.

"I guess I know now who your poor folks will be this year. They haven't a cent to their names, nor a shirt to their backs," laughed Bobby. "But why the tree?"

"Come and help me set it up; then you'll find out," answered Betty.

Such a busy morning as they had after that! Bob set up the tree in the middle of the big barn. Betty made little bundles and hung them on the tree: a package of meat cut fine for Shep, marked with his name in big letters; seven catnip mice hung by their string tails for the seven cats on the farm; four carrots tied in a bunch of hay for Molly, the young horse; four apples tied in hay for Duke, the old gray horse; lumps of sugar for Shep and Duke and Molly.

Then Betty was puzzled. She ran to Uncle Ben. "What does a cow like best?" she asked.

"Well, my cows like cornstalks. There is a pile back of the old barn."

So Betty tied some cornstalks in loose bunches and placed them at the base of the tree. On the floor, she put a big bag of corn for the hens.

After dinner the fun began. Everyone put on a sweater and went to the barn, Shep walking at Betty's heels, proud of his new bow. Not all of

A SURPRISE CHRISTMAS

the cats could be found, but five of them came in answer to Aunt Martha's call. Shep took his meat and without a single "Thank you" ran to an empty stall to eat it. The horses nodded, "Thank you" as they ate the sugar, carrots, and apples that the children held out to them. The cats and kittens played with their catnip mice and lapped up saucers of milk. The cows crunched their cornstalks and looked at the queer antics of the kittens. Bob carried the bag of corn out to the hen yard, and Betty fed the chickens, which crowded around her feet.

When the children went back to the barn with the empty bag, they themselves had a surprise. A gray squirrel had stolen in at the open door and was sitting up on his hind legs under the Christmas tree, eating the corn that had been spilled. He seemed as much at home as if he had been invited to the party.

"I think he must be our poor family," laughed Betty as she threw him another handful of corn.

FATHER'S SURPRISE

"Children!" suddenly called a man's voice from the yard. Only Father called like that. The children turned, and there he stood in the door of the barn, smiling at them. They rushed to his arms. How happy they were to see him!

"So you children had a Christmas tree for the animals, did you?" said Father.

"Well, run into the house with your father, and I'll see what the tree will have for you," said Uncle Tom, who stood just behind their father, his arms loaded with bundles. Soon Uncle Tom called, and everyone went out to the Christmas tree.

"Your Uncle Tom and I must start for home by five o'clock; so you children had better open your presents right now," said Father. Betty and

A SURPRISE CHRISTMAS 345

Bob did not need to be told twice. Eagerly they opened the packages, gay with ribbons and seals. There were books, snowshoes, a red silk umbrella for Betty, and a pair of skating boots for Bob; candy and a gold piece for each from Uncle Tom; and best of all, a little penciled note from Mother to tell them that she was really better and to wish them a Merry Christmas.

"Well," said Bobby as the big car drove out of the yard with Father and Uncle Tom, "this has certainly been a surprise Christmas for us all!"

Notes and Questions

1. What three happenings made a merry Christmas for the children?

2. What did the children say about Christmas that shows they were unselfish?

3. What did Betty just happen to do that gave her the idea for the animals' Christmas party?

4. Explain: *special-delivery, attic, grove, flannel, catnip.*

5. Read lines that tell how Betty decorated the tree.

6. Read lines that tell how the children gave the animals their presents.

You would enjoy "Christmas in Africa," Bradley (in *Alice in Jungleland);* "The Magic Christmas Gift," Fox, and "Sandy's Christmas," Travis (in *Christmas in Storyland,* Van Buren and Bemis).

THE CHRISTMAS FAIRY AND SCROOGE

Charles Dickens

This little play was made from a famous story by Charles Dickens, a great and beloved English story-teller. In it we see old Ebenezer Scrooge, rich, cross, and stingy. To him Christmas was all humbug and foolishness. But one Christmas a kind fairy helped him learn the greatest lesson in the world.

Act I

Time—Christmas Eve
Scene—Scrooge's Sitting-room

Persons:

Scrooge   Scrooge's Nephew   Christmas Fairy

[Scrooge, in dressing-gown, slippers, and nightcap, sits before a fire. He is eating from a bowl of gruel, and his face is scowling. Scrooge's nephew comes in, with his face smiling and his eyes sparkling. He looks cheerful and kind.]

Nephew. A Merry Christmas, uncle!

Scrooge. [*Crossly.*] Bah! Humbug!

Nephew. Christmas a humbug, uncle? You don't mean that, I am sure.

Scrooge. I do. Merry Christmas, indeed! What right have you to be merry? You're poor enough.

Nephew. [*Gayly.*] Come, then! What right have you to be cross? You're rich enough.

THE CHRISTMAS FAIRY AND SCROOGE 347

SCROOGE. Bah! Humbug! You are just like my clerk, Bob Cratchit. He wished me a Merry Christmas today, and he hasn't one sixpence to rub against another.

NEPHEW. Bob Cratchit has something better than sixpences. He has a heart full of kindness and love. Come, don't be cross, uncle!

SCROOGE. What else can I be when I live in such a foolish world? Merry Christmas! Bah! Humbug!

NEPHEW. Oh, no! Uncle!

UNCLE. Nephew! Keep Christmas in your own way and let me keep it in mine.

NEPHEW. Keep it? But you don't keep it!

SCROOGE. Let me leave it alone then. What good has Christmas ever done you?

NEPHEW. Christmas is a kind time, a time to think of those who need help. It is a time when people smile and say cheery words. I believe that Christmas *has* done me good and *will* do me good, and I say, "God bless it!"

SCROOGE. Bah! Humbug!

NEPHEW. It is a time when you might help Bob Cratchit. He needs help. Tiny Tim, his little lame son, needs help.

SCROOGE. Why did you come here? Let Bob Cratchit help himself! I am rich, but who made me rich? Did Christmas?

NEPHEW. Don't be angry, uncle! Come! Have dinner with us tomorrow. You must be lonely.

SCROOGE. I never give dinners to anyone, and I never take them with anyone. A foolish custom! If you have nothing better to say, good night!

NEPHEW. [*Going to his uncle and offering him his hand.*] Let us be friends.

SCROOGE. [*Angrily turning away.*] Good night!

NEPHEW. I am sorry to find you so cross, but I

THE CHRISTMAS FAIRY AND SCROOGE 349

will not quarrel with you. It is Christmas Eve, and Christmas should make us cheerful and happy. So, a Merry Christmas, uncle!

SCROOGE. [*Still more angrily.*] Good night!

NEPHEW. And a Happy New Year!

SCROOGE. [*Standing up, waving spoon toward the door and almost shouting.*] GOOD NIGHT!

[Scrooge's nephew goes out. Scrooge sits by the fire, scraping the bowl and scowling. Suddenly, bells begin to ring gayly. The door opens, and the Christmas Fairy, young and beautiful, comes in. A bright star shines on her forehead, and she holds a wand of holly.]

CHRISTMAS FAIRY. A Merry Christmas to you!

SCROOGE. [*He looks up suddenly.*] Bah! Humbug! You are the third foolish person who has said that to me today! Who are you, and what do you want?

FAIRY. In good time you shall learn who I am. I am here because you need me. I have a Christmas gift for you.

SCROOGE. Christmas gift? Humbug! I am rich. I need no gifts. I take nothing, and I give nothing.

FAIRY. And so you *have* nothing! You are rich, but what good does your money do? Does it make you happy? Does it make anyone else happy? Do you help anyone with it? Your clerk, Bob Cratchit, is very poor. He works hard for you, but you pay him as little as you can. He needs help. You are rich. Will you help him?

SCROOGE. [*Angrily.*] Bob Cratchit! Bob Cratchit! You are as foolish as my nephew. And Bob Cratchit is foolish, too. He wished me a Merry

THE CHRISTMAS FAIRY AND SCROOGE 351

Christmas today! Merry Christmas, indeed! He hasn't a sixpence to make merry with!

FAIRY. Bob Cratchit has something better than sixpences. He has something that all your money cannot buy. But he needs help. Will you help him? His son, Tiny Tim, is ill and lame. If you help him, he can get strong and well. Will you help him?

SCROOGE. I help nobody. Let Bob Cratchit help himself. That is what I do. If he has something better than sixpences, let him use it, I say.

FAIRY. Yes, Bob Cratchit has something better than sixpences. He has a kind and loving heart. But your heart is hard, Ebenezer Scrooge. You have no friends. You help nobody. You never say a kind word. You are cross and stingy.

SCROOGE. [*Waving his spoon angrily.*] Go away!

FAIRY. Not until I have given you a Christmas gift. Do you know what Christmas gift you need, Ebenezer Scrooge? You need a kind and loving heart. I will help you get it. I am the Christmas Fairy. This is Christmas Eve, and I will show you Bob Cratchit's poor little home on Christmas day. You shall see that kind and loving hearts are better than riches, and that poor Bob Cratchit is happier than you.

SCROOGE. Bah! Humbug!
FAIRY. [*Waving wand.*] Look! Ebenezer Scrooge, what do you see?

[The Fairy points with her wand to the farther end of the room. Scrooge scowls and looks, then stares in surprise.]

ACT II

Time—CHRISTMAS EVE
Scene—SCROOGE'S SITTING-ROOM

Persons:

SCROOGE   THE FAIRY   MRS. CRATCHIT   BOB CRATCHIT
THE CRATCHIT CHILDREN: MARTHA, BELINDA, PETER, FANNY, DICK, TINY TIM.

[Scrooge sits by the fire, staring at the other end of the room. The Christmas Fairy stands beside him. As Scrooge stares, he looks first surprised, then sorry, then ashamed.

An odd change has come over the other end of the room. It looks like the kitchen of a poor home. There is an open brick fireplace, with a hook from which hangs a kettle. A saucepan is on the hob. A table stands in the middle of the room, and some chairs are against the wall. Everything is very poor but very clean.

All the people in the room are very poor but very clean. The children's faces shine with much scrubbing; Mrs. Cratchit and Belinda are happy in cheap, bright ribbons. Master Peter Cratchit is wearing a very high collar, his father's; he is very proud of it, but its sharp corners are always in the way.

Mrs. Cratchit, with Belinda's help, puts the cloth on the table. Master Peter Cratchit plunges a fork into the saucepan of potatoes, his big collar getting into his mouth

as he does so. Fanny and Dick come tearing into the
room and dance about the table.]

DICK. Oh, Mother! We have been to the baker's
shop.

FANNY. We smelled our goose, Mother! The
baker says it is nearly done. There are a dozen
geese in his big oven. Oh, how good they smell!

DICK. And the sage and onions, too. Oh! oh! oh! oh!

[The two children dance up and down.]

FANNY. Oh, Dick, see Peter's new collar! How
fine he looks in it!

DICK. It is father's collar. Some day I can have
one of father's collars, too. Then I will go to
walk in the Park. Doesn't Peter look beautiful?

[They dance around Peter.]

MRS. CRATCHIT. Where can your dear father be?
And your brother, Tiny Tim? And Martha
wasn't as late as this last Christmas!

[Martha comes in.]

FANNY. Here's Martha, Mother. Oh, Martha,
there's such a goose in the baker's oven!

MRS. CRATCHIT. [*Taking off Martha's bonnet and
shawl, and kissing her half a dozen times.*] Why,
bless your heart, my dear, how late you are!

MARTHA. We worked till very late in the shop last night. Then we had to get up early this morning to clear everything away.

MRS. CRATCHIT. Well, never mind, so long as you have come. Sit down before the fire, my dear, and get warm.

DICK. Here's Father coming! Hide, Martha, hide!

[Martha hides behind the door as Bob Cratchit comes in. One end of a comforter hangs down before him, and the rest is wound tightly about his neck. His worn clothes are carefully mended and brushed. Tiny Tim, holding a crutch in his hand, is on his father's shoulder.]

BOB CRATCHIT. [*Looking around.*] Why, where's our Martha?

FANNY AND DICK. Not coming!

BOB CRATCHIT. [*Surprised and disappointed.*] Not coming? On Christmas Day?

[He puts Tiny Tim down.]

MRS. CRATCHIT. We must not make Father sad with our jokes. No, Martha is not coming, because she is already here.

MARTHA. [*Running out.*] Here I am, Father! Merry Christmas to you!

BOB CRATCHIT. [*His good-natured face covered with smiles.*] How glad I am to see you, Martha! It does your father good to have all his children with him on Christmas Day.

THE CHRISTMAS FAIRY AND SCROOGE

DICK. Come here, Tiny Tim! Hurry, hurry! You can hear the Christmas pudding singing in the kettle.

[He helps Tiny Tim over to the fireplace.]

FANNY. Hear it bubble and boil! It's all tied up in a cloth. See it steam!

DICK. It smells like washing day!

FANNY. That's the cloth.

DICK. And it smells just like the baker's shop!

FANNY. That's the pudding.

DICK. Oh, but it smells like a fruit shop, too!

FANNY. That's the raisins and currants.

[Fanny and Dick dance about the fireplace and sniff the pudding. Tiny Tim waves his little crutch.]

TINY TIM. Hurrah! Hurrah!

MRS. CRATCHIT. [*Softly.*] How did Tiny Tim behave at church?

BOB CRATCHIT. As good as gold. He sits alone so much that he has strange thoughts. He told me coming home that he hoped the people saw him in the church, because he was a cripple. He said it might be pleasant for them to remember on Christmas Day Who it was that made cripples walk and blind men see.

MRS. CRATCHIT. [*Wiping her eyes.*] Oh, if we only had a little more money, we could get him medicine and better food. We could send him into the country for better air. Why doesn't Scrooge pay you fairly for your work? Then we could help Tiny Tim, and he would get well again.

BOB CRATCHIT. [*Shaking his finger at her.*] My dear! Christmas Day!

MRS. CRATCHIT. You know it is true, Bob Cratchit, but you are too kind-hearted to say so.

BELINDA. [*Breaking in on them.*] Isn't it time for Peter to get the goose, Mother?

THE CHRISTMAS FAIRY AND SCROOGE 357

Fanny and Dick. May we go, too? Oh, let us go!

Peter. I'll carry Tiny Tim on my shoulder. Fanny and Dick can bring home the goose.

Fanny. Oh, yes! We'll be very careful. Do let Tiny Tim go with us! He can see the goose and smell the sage and onions all the way home.

Belinda. Here is the platter.

[Bob Cratchit puts Tiny Tim upon Peter's shoulder, and the four children go out together.]

Bob Cratchit. [*Going up to Mrs. Cratchit.*] I have found work for Peter, at last. It is hard, and the pay is small, but it will help us a little.

Martha. Just think of Peter's being a man of business!

Bob Cratchit. I hope he will not have to work as many hours a day as poor Martha, here. But how happy I am that I have such good children and that they are so willing to work!

Mrs. Cratchit. [*Hurrying to the fireplace.*] I must make the gravy. Belinda, will you mash the potatoes and, Martha, you may sweeten the apple-sauce and put the plates on the table.

[In a few moments Fanny and Dick bring in the goose on the platter; it is a very small goose, but they carry it proudly. Peter follows, with Tiny Tim on his shoulder. Bob Cratchit lifts Tiny Tim down carefully, while Mrs. Cratchit takes the platter and sets it on the table. They all stand around the table looking at the goose.]

PETER. Oh! What a goose! What a fine, large goose! Was there ever such a goose before?

[Fanny and Dick hurry to set the chairs about the table.]

MRS. CRATCHIT. Dinner is ready, children. Sit down, everyone. Peter, lift Tiny Tim into his little chair.

TINY TIM. [*Waving his arms.*] Hurrah! Hurrah! Hurrah!

BOB CRATCHIT. Before we begin, let us all wish a Merry Christmas to Mr. Scrooge. He gives me work, or I could not pay for this good dinner. If it were not for him, we should not have this fat goose steaming here on the table.

[Bob Cratchit stands up, with carving knife in hand, ready to carve the goose. Tiny Tim and Fanny and Dick beat upon the table with the handles of their knives.]

MRS. CRATCHIT. [*Looking up angrily.*] Mr. Scrooge, indeed! I wish I had him here! I'd give him a piece of my mind to feast upon, and I hope he'd have a good appetite for it! Mr. Scrooge, indeed!

BOB CRATCHIT. My dear! Think of the children! And this is Christmas Day!

MRS. CRATCHIT. It *should* be Christmas Day, indeed! On what other day could we give good

THE CHRISTMAS FAIRY AND SCROOGE

wishes to such a stingy, selfish man? [*Shaking her finger gently at her husband.*] You know he is, Bob! Nobody knows it better than you do, poor fellow. Don't you work hard all day for very little pay? Does he ever give you a pleasant word? Look at poor Tiny Tim! If you were paid what you earn, we could get help for him. Then he might walk again.

BOB CRATCHIT. [*Shaking his head.*] My dear! Just to please me! Christmas Day!

MRS. CRATCHIT. Well, then! I'll wish him a Merry Christmas for your sake, and for the sake of Christmas. A Merry Christmas and a Happy New Year to Mr. Scrooge!

ALL. A Merry Christmas and a Happy New Year to Mr. Scrooge!

BOB CRATCHIT. A Merry Christmas to us all, my dears! God bless us.

TINY TIM. God bless us, every one!

ACT III

Time—CHRISTMAS EVE
Scene—SCROOGE'S SITTING-ROOM

Persons:

CHRISTMAS FAIRY   SCROOGE

[Scrooge stands looking eagerly into the far end of the room; but it is no longer a little kitchen. The noisy, happy Cratchits have disappeared. He turns and looks at the Christmas Fairy, who stands at his side. Scrooge's face looks sad and softened by what he has seen, and when he speaks, his voice is gentle and kind.]

SCROOGE. [*Eagerly.*] Tell me, was it all a dream?

CHRISTMAS FAIRY. That depends on you, Ebenezer Scrooge.

SCROOGE. I have been wrong; I see it! I have been cross and selfish, and even cruel.

FAIRY. [*Smiling at the change in Scrooge.*] Did you see anything better than sixpences?

SCROOGE. Yes; love is better than sixpences. A kind heart is better than sixpences. It is better than all the riches in the world. Tell me! Will Tiny Tim live?

FAIRY. Tell me! Will you take my Christmas gift? Will you change your hard heart for a kind one?

SCROOGE. [*Eagerly.*] I will try! I will try!

FAIRY. Then Tiny Tim will live, because you will help him.

SCROOGE. [*Quickly and eagerly.*] I will raise Bob Cratchit's wages! I'll pay him every sixpence he earns. I'll send him the biggest turkey in London for his Christmas dinner. I saw one today. It was twice as big as Tiny Tim. I'll send that one! [*He laughs and waves his spoon joyfully.*] And I'll send Tiny Tim to the country for better air. He shall have fresh milk and cream and eggs! Yes, and Martha shall go with him to take care of him, and to have a rest! Hurrah! Hurrah! [*Waves spoon.*] Oh, I have been foolish, but I have learned a lesson. [*He turns to the Fairy.*] A Merry Christmas to you! A Merry Christmas to everybody! A Happy New Year to all the world!

Notes and Questions

1. Read the last sentence on page 351 and then tell what lesson the Fairy wanted Scrooge to learn. Did Scrooge learn it? Find lines on page 361 to prove your answer.

2. What reason did Scrooge give for believing that Bob Cratchit could not possibly be happy?

3. Tell one thing to show that Scrooge's meanness caused suffering to others.

4. What three things did Scrooge promise to do to show that he had learned his lesson?

5. (a) From this list of four titles, choose one for Act I of the play, and one for Act III.

>How Ebenezer Scrooge Celebrated Christmas
>The Christmas Fairy Visits Scrooge
>Scrooge Learns the True Christmas Spirit
>Happiness Comes to the Cratchit Family

(b) Make up a title for Act II.

6. Name the three most important people in the play (other than the Fairy), and tell in a few words what each person was like.

7. Be ready to read lines spoken by the Fairy that show what kind of man Scrooge was.

8. Read the lines that best tell what kind of time Christmas is.

Other Christmas stories are "The Christmas Cuckoo," Browne (in *Child-Library Readers, Book Four*); *The Birds' Christmas Carol,* Wiggin; and "The Christmas Apple," Sawyer (in *This Way to Christmas,* Chapter IV).

A NEW YEAR'S LEAF

Elizabeth Thornton Turner

Today you turn a fair new leaf;
'Tis clean and white and plain.
Don't let a careless breeze rush in
And turn it back again!

HEARTS WERE MADE TO GIVE AWAY[*]

Annette Wynne

Hearts were made to give away
On Valentine's good day;
Wrap them up in dainty white,
Send them off the thirteenth night,
Any kind of heart that's handy—
Hearts of lace, and hearts of candy,
Hearts all trimmed with ribbands fine,
Send for good St. Valentine.
Hearts were made to give away
On Valentine's dear day.

[*]Reprinted by permission from *For Days and Days: A Year-round Treasury of Verse for Children*, by Annette Wynne. Copyright, 1919, by Frederick A. Stokes Company.

WHO SHALL BE MAY QUEEN?

Phila Butler Bowman

Much as we love winter with its happy times at Thanksgiving and Christmas, we are all glad when Maytime comes. What pleasure it is to find the first flowers, to see the leaves slowly come out on the trees, and to welcome our bird friends back from their winter homes! If you read this story carefully, you will learn some interesting things about spring.

Out in the May meadow the wild grapevine was flinging itself around a slender young tree.

"What a beautiful Maypole the grapevine has made of the tree!" said Jack-in-the-Pulpit. "Let's have a May party, now that we have a Maypole."

"Hurrah!" cried the wild flowers, who at once began talking about who should be May Queen.

"I was the first flower up," said the Crocus. "I think I should be chosen."

"Oh, no!" said the Arbutus. "I was cuddled down under my leaves, keeping warm, and saw you rubbing your eyes long after I was awake."

"I think it ought to be a tall flower," said the Hyacinth; "and fragrant."

"Because you know you are both," laughed the Trillium; "but how about the Lilac? She is taller than you and just as fragrant."

WHO SHALL BE MAY QUEEN? 365

"Well," said the Hyacinth good-naturedly, "it would be fine to have a May party, no matter who is May Queen. But who is to decide for us? Shall we let Jack-in-the-Pulpit decide? We might ask the Lilies-of-the-Valley. They are so sweet they would never choose one of their own family."

"Why couldn't the Bluebird be May Queen?" asked the Violet, who loved her.

"I think," said the Easter Bunny, coming suddenly out from behind his log, "that we could choose a better May Queen than anyone you have named. The May Queen should be someone as happy as the birds; someone whom everybody loves; and someone as fresh and beautiful as the flowers."

"Caw! Caw!" croaked the Raven. "Where will you find anyone in all the world like that?"

Suddenly a little Child came running lightly through the wood. She sang as she came, and her song was a song of the May sky, and her laugh was like the sound of the rippling spring brook.

A little Elf was hiding in the fern. Suddenly he stole out and whispered to Jack-in-the-Pulpit:

"The little Child is the best Queen of May."

"Crown the little Child!" cried Jack-in-the-Pulpit. "Crown her! Crown her Queen of the May!"

cried all the flowers, till the trees shook with laughter.

Then the little Child danced for joy, and the Elf brought Trillium blossoms and wove them with Crocus for a crown. He hung the Arbutus in pink clusters around her waist. He gave her Hyacinth for a scepter, and poured Dandelion gold at her feet. Then the Child laughed so merrily that all the other little Children came running, and they danced about the wonderful Maypole till they set all the Bluebells ringing.

When the day was over and the little Children

were sleeping in their soft, white beds, dreaming of the beautiful day, the flowers talked to one another in the starlight.

"There was never such a wonderful May Day before," said the Hyacinth.

"We will have a May party again next year," said the Crocus.

"And we will all come," said the Arbutus; "and I shall get there first, I know."

"And always," said the Bluebird, as she looked into the Violet's eyes, "the little Child shall be Queen of May."

Notes and Questions

1. From this story, which do you think was the first spring flower?

2. Make a list of several flowers named in this story. Opposite each flower write the color or colors of the flower.

3. Be ready to read lines that tell—
   (a) What kind of person the May Queen should be.
   (b) How the Elf decorated the May Queen.

You would enjoy reading "The First May Baskets," Wickes (in *A Child's Book of Holiday Plays*); "The Robin and the Rose," Bowman (in *The Little Brown Bowl*); and "May Day," Stewart (in *The Birds Began to Sing*).

A BACKWARD LOOK

EACH holiday has its own special kind of celebration. Christmas means giving and receiving presents. On birthdays we make others happy with presents and best wishes. Thanksgiving makes us think of a feast of good things to eat. Fourth of July calls to mind fireworks, games, and parades. What a sad world this would be without holidays!

But there is something more to a holiday than these things we do: there is a spirit, or feeling, that we should have. Turn back to page 319 and read the last two lines of the little poem there. Where must Christmas really begin? Who in these stories did not have Christmas in his heart? The Cratchits were poor, and Father and Mother Cratchit were worried about Tiny Tim's health; but they were happy on Christmas. There was Christmas in their hearts. How did the Pilgrims show, on the first day of their festival, that Thanksgiving was in their hearts? On the Fourth of July, what spirit should you have in your heart?

Of course your family celebrated Christmas for you when you were just a baby. You probably received rattles and other toys, but you did not know what it all meant. Can you tell the true meaning of some of the holidays now?

If you will turn to page 374, you will find a list of books that have some other good stories about holidays. You would enjoy reading them.

GOOD BOOKS TO READ

Part One. The Outdoor World

More about Animals, by Margery Bianco. Macmillan
Pollwiggle's Progress, by Wilfred S. Bronson. Macmillan
The Burgess Flower Book for Children, by Thornton Waldo Burgess. Little
The Smaller Birds, by Eric Fitch Daglish. Morrow
Real Nature Stories, by Clara J. Denton. Whitman, A.
Uncle Sam's Animals, by Frances Margaret Fox. Appleton-Century
Fly-Aways and Other Seed Travelers, by Francis Marion Fultz. Public-School
The Wonders of the Jungle, Book One, by Sarath Ghosh. Heath
Gray Squirrel, by Joseph Wharton Lippincott. Penn
Kari the Elephant, by Dhan Gopal Mukerji. Dutton
Fuzzy and His Neighbors, by José F. Nonindez. Appleton-Century
And That's Why, by William Maxwell Reed. Harcourt
Wilderness Babies, by Julia A. Schwartz. Little
Woodland Tales, by Ernest Thompson Seton. Doubleday
A Child's Book of Country Stories, by Jessie Smith. Dial Press
Zeke the Raccoon, by Rhea Wells. Viking Press
Jemmie, the Kitten from Maine, by Eleanor Wheeler. Random

Part Two. Little American Citizens

Stories of Pioneer Life for Young Readers, by Florence Bass. Heath
You Can't Pet a Possum, by Arna Bontemps. Morrow
The True Story of Abraham Lincoln, by Elbridge S. Brooks. Lothrop

Stories of American Life and Adventure, by Edward Eggleston. Am. Bk.
Stories of Great Americans for Little Americans, by Edward Eggleston. Am. Bk.
Queen of the Pirate Isle, by Bret Harte. Warne
Lucinda: A Little Girl of 1860, by Mabel Leigh Hunt. Stokes
Peter Pocket: A Little Boy of the Cumberland Mountains, by May Justus. Doubleday
Little Fox, by Katharine Louise Keelor. Macmillan
Little Indians, by Mrs. Mabel La Rue. Macmillan
The Pioneer Twins and *The Puritan Twins,* by Lucy Fitch Perkins. Houghton
Stories of the Pilgrims, by Margaret B. Pumphrey. Rand
Nancy Rutledge, by Katharine Pyle. Little
Robin on the Mountain, by Charlie May Simon. Dutton
A Little Girl of Long Ago, by Eliza Orne White. Houghton
Little House in the Big Woods, by Laura Ingalls Wilder. Harper

Part Three. Boys and Girls of Other Lands

Popo and Fifina: Children of Haiti, by Arna Bontemps and Langston Hughes. Macmillan
Alice in Jungleland, by Mary Hastings Bradley. Appleton-Century
The Little Swiss Wood Carver, by Madeline Brandeis. Grosset
Our Little Friends of the Arabian Desert, Adi and Hamda, by Frances Carpenter. Am. Bk.
Handsome Donkey, by Mary Gould Davis. Harcourt
My Boys: A Holiday Book for Big and Little, by Gustaf af Geigerstam. Viking Press
Little Tonino, by Helen Hill and Violet Maxwell. Macmillan
Fortune's Caravan, by Mme. Lily Javal. Morrow

Peter and Gretchen of Old Nuremburg, by Viola M. Jones. Whitman, A.

Little Pear and His Friends, by Eleanore Frances Lattimore. Harcourt

Children of the Mountain Eagle, by Elizabeth Cleveland Miller. Doubleday

Anton and Trini: Children of the Alpland, by Virginia Olcott. Silver

Jean and Fanchon: Children of Fair France, by Virginia Olcott. Silver

Wanda and Greta at Broby Farm, by Amy Palm. Longmans

Kit and Kat: More Adventures of the Dutch Twins, by Lucy Fitch Perkins. Houghton

The Swiss Twins, by Lucy Fitch Perkins. Houghton

The Spanish Twins, by Lucy Fitch Perkins. Houghton

A Scotch Circus, by Tom Powers. Houghton

Olaf, Lofoten Fisherman, by Constance Wiel Schram. Longmans

One Day with Jambi in Sumatra, by Armstrong Sperry. Winston

Moni, by Johanna Spyri. Lippincott

A Day on Skates: The Story of a Dutch Picnic, by Hilda Van Stockum. Harper

Coco the Goat, by Rhea Wells. Doubleday

PART FOUR. STORIES EVERYONE SHOULD KNOW

Lulu's Library, by Louisa May Alcott. Little
Fairy Tales from Hans Christian Andersen, translated by Mrs. E. Lucas. Dutton
Wizard of Oz, by Frank L. Baum. Bobbs
Lonesomest Doll, by Abbie Farwell Brown. Houghton
Little Lord Fauntleroy, by Frances Hodgson Burnett. Scribner
Made-to-Order Stories, by Dorothy Canfield. Harcourt

The Adventures of Pinocchio, by C. Collodi. Macmillan
The Little Lame Prince, by Dinah Maria Craik. Macmillan
The Three Mulla-mulgars, by Walter De La Mare. Knopf
Monkey That Would Not Kill, by Henry Drummond. Dodd
Lob Lie-by-the-Fire, and Other Stories, by Juliana Ewing. Harcourt
The Snow Maiden, by Georgene Faulkner. Grosset
Some Poems of Childhood, by Eugene Field. Scribner
Just Across the Street, by Rachel Field. Macmillan
The Coffee-Pot Face (poems), by Aileen L. Fisher. McBride
Forty Good-Night Tales, by Rose Fyleman. Doubleday
The History of Little Goody Two Shoes, by Oliver Goldsmith. Heath
Garden of Eden: Stories from the First Nine Books of the Old Testament, by George Hodges. Houghton
The Complete Nonsense Book, by Edward Lear. Little
Sung Under the Silver Umbrella: Poems for Young Children, by the Literature Committee of the Association for Childhood Education. Macmillan
The Story of Dr. Dolittle, by Hugh Lofting. Stokes
The Children's Blue Bird, by Mme. Maurice Maeterlinck. Dodd
Winnie-the-Pooh, by A. A. Milne. Dutton
The House at Pooh Corner, by A. A. Milne. Dutton
Arkansas Bear, by Albert Bigelow Paine. Altemus
The Christ Child, by Maud and Miska Petersham. Doubleday
Silver Pennies: A Collection of Modern Poems for Boys and Girls, by Blanche Jennings Thompson. Macmillan
Skipping Along Alone (poems), by Winifred Welles. Macmillan
Magic Forest, by Stewart Edward White. Macmillan
Tales of Laughter, by Kate Douglas Wiggin and Nora Archibald Smith. Doubleday

PART FIVE. BUSY WORKERS AND THEIR WORK

Boys and Girls of Colonial Days, by Carolyn Sherwin Bailey. Flanagan

The Story of Money, by Mary Carter. Farrar

Big Fellow at Work, by Dorothy Baruch. Harper

The Little Black Coal, by Ethel Cook Eliot. Stokes

How the Derrick Works, by Wilfred Jones. Macmillan

Diggers and Builders, by Henry B. Lent. Macmillan

Clear Track Ahead! by Henry B. Lent. Macmillan

Story of Books Up through the Ages, by Lambert Mitchell Naumburg. Harper

Farmer Sows His Wheat, by Adele Gutman Nathan. Minton

Little Blacknose, by Hildegarde Hoyt Swift. Harcourt

Playing with Clay, by Ida W. Wheeler. Macmillan

PART SIX. FAMOUS HEROES OF LONG AGO

Stories of Great Adventures, by Carolyn Sherwin Bailey. Bradley

Fifty Famous People: A Book of Short Stories, by James Baldwin. Am. Bk.

The Story of Siegfried, by James Baldwin. Scribner

True Story of Christopher Columbus, by Elbridge Streeter Brooks. Lothrop

Tales of Romance, Andrew Lang. Longmans

Joan of Arc, by Boutet de Monvel. McKay

Mighty Men from Achilles to Julius Caesar, by Eleanor Farjeon. Appleton-Century

Men of Old Greece, by Jennie Hall. Little

Great People of the Past, by Rhoda D. Power. Macmillan

Little Jarvis, by Molly Elliot Seawell. Appleton-Century

PART SEVEN. HOLIDAYS AND FESTIVALS

Why the Chimes Rang, by Raymond MacDonald Alden. Bobbs

Merry Tales for Children, by Carolyn Bailey. Bradley

Apple Tree, by Margery Bianco. Doubleday

Our Holidays in Poetry, by Carnegie Library School Association. Wilson

Christmas: A Book of Stories Old and New, compiled by Alice Dalgliesh. Scribner

Santa Claus on a Lark, and Other Christmas Stories, by Washington Gladden. Appleton-Century

This Way to Christmas, by Ruth Sawyer. Harper

Book of Christmas Stories for Children, by Maude Owen Walters. Dodd

The Birds' Christmas Carol, by Kate Douglas Wiggin. Houghton

For Days and Days (poems), by Annette Wynne. Stokes

GLOSSARY

PRONUNCIATION KEY

The pronunciation of each word is shown just after the word, in this way: **ac tive** (ak′tiv). The letters and signs used have sounds as in the words shown below. The accented syllable is marked ′. Some long words have the main accent (′) and a lesser or "secondary" accent (′). These are shown by two accent marks, the heavier one being the main accent.

a	at, can	ȧ	beggar, opera	o	on, not	u	up, but
ā	came, face	e	end, bend	ō	more, open	ū	use, pure
ä	far, father	ē	be, equal	ö	to, move	u̇	put, full
â	all, ball	ė	her, certain	ô	off, song	ṵ	nature
à	ask	ẹ	towel, prudent	ǫ	actor, second	ṭ	picture
ã	care, dare	i	it, pin	oi	oil, point	th	thin
ạ	alone, company	ī	line, mine	ou	out, found	ᴛʜ	then

A single dot under ā, ē, ō, ö, or ū means that the sound is a little shorter and lighter, as in cot′tạge, rẹ-duce′, gas′ọ-line, in′tọ, ụ-nī′ted.

A

ac cord, of their own accord (ạ-kôrd′), freely; without his thinking about it

ac tive (ak′tiv), quick in moving about

aid (ād), help

air-tight, closed so tightly that no air can get in or out

an te lope (an′tẹ-lōp), an animal somewhat like a deer

an tics (an′tiks), playful tricks

an vil (an′vil), an iron block on which metal is hammered into different shapes

anx ious (angk′shus), worried; uneasy

a pol o gies (ạ-pol′ọ-jiz), excuses

ap peared (ạ-pērd′), seemed; came in sight

ap proached (ạ-prōcht′), came close to

ar bu tus (är-bū′tus), a wild plant with fragrant pink and white blossoms that come early in the spring

ar mor (är′mǫr), covering made of steel worn by fighting men of long ago

ar ray, glad array (ạ-rā′), rich or beautiful clothing

ar ri val (ạ-rī′vạl), coming to or reaching a place

a stir (ạ-stėr′), moving

a stride (ạ-strīd′), with one leg on each side

at tic (at′ik), a room next to the roof of a house

B

bade him (bad), told him to
bargain (bär′gan), one promise given in exchange for another; a trade
Baucis (bâ′sis)
Belgium (bel′ji-um), a small country in western Europe
bellows (bel′ōz), a tool for blowing a fire to make it burn
Beowulf (bā′ō-wulf)
bin, a box for holding things
blast (blåst), sound made by blowing a horn or a trumpet
bleating (blē′ting), crying like a sheep or a goat
blunt, not sharp, not pointed
boast (bōst), a bragging speech
bodice (bod′is), a close-fitting sleeveless jacket, low-necked, and usually laced in front. See picture on page 191.
bonny (bon′i), beautiful
bounded, leaped quickly
boxed his ears, struck him on his ears with her paw
bray (brā), make a loud, harsh cry or noise
breadth (bredth), distance from side to side; width
brew (brö), make a drink of some kind
Briar Patch (brī′ar), a group of thorny or prickly bushes
brisk, quick; nimble; lively
brood (bröd), a number of young birds hatched at the same time, or cared for together
Bruin (brö′in), a name for the brown bear
Brunhild (brön′hilt)
brushwood, small branches of trees
bustled (bus′ld), moved about quickly
butternut, a kind of walnut

C

canal (ka-nal′), a long, deep ditch dug to carry water
canvas (kan′vas), a kind of coarse, heavy cloth
carpet-bag, traveling bag made of carpet instead of leather
cathedral (ka-thē′dral), a large, beautiful church
catnip, a plant which cats like
central (sen′tral), middle
chamois (sham′i), a small animal something like a goat, that lives in high mountains
Charlemagne (shär′le-mān)
charmed, delighted
chuckled (chuk′ld), said with a laugh
clad, dressed
cliffs, high, steep rocks
clump, several bushes or plants growing close together
clusters, bunches
colony (kol′ō-ni), a small village or settlement
comforter (kum′for-tėr), a long woolen scarf. See picture on page 355.
committee (ko-mit′ē), a number of people chosen to do a certain thing
companion (kom-pan′yon), one who goes along with another person
comrade (kom′rad), friend; companion
Congress (kong′gres), the men who meet and make laws for our country
conquered (kong′kėrd), overcome
conversation (kon-vėr-sā′shon), talk
copybook, ruled blank book used for practice in writing
Cornwallis (kôrn-wol′is)
crags, rough, high rocks

GLOSSARY 377

croaked (krōkt), said in a low, hoarse voice
crunched (truncht), chewed noisily
cunning, small and pleasing to look at; sly, like a fox
curious (kū′ri-us), strange; wanting to know things
custom (kus′tom), a way of doing things

D

dame, an old woman; a lady; **Royal Dame**, the Queen
Danes (dānz), people who lived in what is now Denmark, Norway, and Sweden
darted, dashed
decayed (dē-kād′), spoiled
deceive (dē-sēv′), cheat; pretend to another
decorated (dek′ō-rā-ted), painted; trimmed
delicate (del′i-kat), small and slender
delicious (dē-lish′us), very pleasant-tasting; sweet-tasting
depth, distance from front to back
desire (dē-zīr′), wish
dikes, dams or banks of earth built to keep out water
disagreeable (dis-a-grē′a-bl), unpleasant, bad-tempered
discouraged (dis-kur′ajd), ready to give up; sad; not cheerful
disturbed (dis-tėrbd′), kept from resting; bothered; worried
dome, a high, round roof
doubtless (dout′les), certainly; probably
dreary (drēr′i), sad; without cheer
drunk his fill, had all the water he wanted

ducked, quickly lowered his head
Dutch (duch), the people of Holland

E

earthen (ėr′thn), made of baked clay
elder (el′dėr), older
Elise (ē-lēs′)
embraced (em-brāst′), wrapped about; hugged
enemies (en′e-miz), things that will harm
ere (ār), before
erect (ē-rekt′), straight up; not bent
events (ē-vents′), happenings
exclaimed, cried out

F

fame, of mighty fame, very well-known
fellow creatures (fel′ō krē′tŭrz), other people
fertile (fėr′til), having rich soil
festivals (fes′ti-valz), times of merrymaking or celebrating special days
filed out, marched out, one behind the other
finally (fī′nal-i), at last
firmly, held fast; kept in place
flannel, a kind of soft wool cloth
fleece, the wool that covers a sheep
fluid (flö′id), a liquid like milk or water
forge (fōrj), place to heat metal so it may be hammered into any shape

---
at, cāme, fär, âll, ȧsk, cāre, a̱lone; end, bē, hėr, towe̱l; it, līne; on, mōre, tö, ôff, acto̱r; oil, out; up, ūse, put, natŭre; pictu̱re; th, thin; ŦH, then. See full key on p. 375.

for tu nate ly (fôr′tū-nāt-li), by good luck
for tune (fôr′tūn), good luck; happy chance
fra grant (frā′grant), sweet-smelling
frisking, dancing and jumping about in play
frock, dress
fu el (fū′el), something to burn in a fire for cooking or heating

G

Ganelon (gan′e-lon)
gasp (gȧsp), a quick catching of the breath
gazed, looked a long time
gen tian (jen′shan), a wild flower, nearly always blue in color
gild ed (gil′ded), made to look like gold
glare (glâr), a very strong light
gleaming, shining brightly
glid ed (glī′ded), moved along smoothly and evenly
glint, the shine of something bright
glittering, shining with light; sparkling
glow of cheer (glō), a feeling of happiness
goatherd (gōt′hèrd), a person who looks after a herd of goats; a goat boy
goodly, large
Goths (goths)
gourd (gōrd), a fruit whose dried shell is sometimes used as a dipper or water bottle
Grand Place, a large open square in a town or city
grasp (grȧsp), hold; seize with the hand
grateful, thankful
grazed, fed on growing grass
Gren del (gren′del)
grid i ron (grid′ī′ern), broiler
grove, a group of trees standing together
gru el (grö′el), a thin porridge
guard, on guard (gärd), watching carefully
guest (gest), a person visiting in the home of another.

H

Ha pan a (hä-pän′ä)
har bor (här′bor), a place along the shore where ships may be safe from storms
hast y (hās′ti), quick; hurried
hauled (hâld), pulled; dragged
heap, pile
hearti est (här′ti-est), most friendly
heav y-heart ed (hev′i-här′ted), very sad
helmet, a piece of armor for the head, worn by soldiers, firemen, etc.
herb (èrb), a plant whose leaves or roots are used for medicine
hide, the skin of an animal
hith er and thith er (hiᴛʜ′èr; ᴛʜiᴛʜ′-èr), here and there
hob, a shelf built at the side of an open fireplace, on which food may be kept warm
hos pi tal i ty (hos-pi-tal′i-ti), food and shelter given in a kind and friendly manner
host ess (hōs′tes), a woman who has a guest in her home
Hroth gar (hrōth′gär)
hud dled (hud′ld), drawn up in a little pile
hum bly (hum′bli), poorly; plainly
humbug, nonsense; make-believe

GLOSSARY 379

I

im me di ate ly (i-mē′di-ạt-li), at once
im mense ly (i-mens′li), very greatly
inn, hotel
in stant (in′stạnt), moment
isles (īlz), small islands

J

Je han Daas (yā′hän däs)
jos tling (jos′ling), pushing or crowding in passing
jour ney-cake (jėr′ni-kāk), a kind of bread made of corn-meal
Jun gle land (jung′gl-land), the middle part of Africa, which is full of thick forests and high mountains

K

keen of eye, able to see well
kid, a young goat

L

lair (lãr), a den or resting-place
lance (làns), a long pole with a sharp steel head, used in fighting or hunting
lashed, beat. The tails of the fish beat the water.
La van da (lä-vän′dä)
lend an ear, hear; listen to
liberty, freedom
lime, fruit like a lemon, but smaller, greener, and sourer
linden tree, a shade-tree with heart-shaped leaves
linked, joined together
lodg ing (loj′ing), a place to stay
loft (lôft), a place just beneath the roof
longed for, wished for very much

M

Mame to (mäm-tō′)
man sion (man′shọn), a large, fine house
Mar sil i us (mär-sil′i-us)
mart (märt), a market-place
mar vel ous (mär′vẹ-lus), wonderful
Mas sa soit (mas′ạ-soit)
mel low (mel′ō), soft and rich
midg et (mij′et), a very tiny person; a dwarf
midst, middle
mighty, very great or strong
Mi nou (mē-nö′)
minstrel, musician; story-teller
mi rac u lous (mi-rak′ụ-lus), wonderful or magical
mod eled after (mod′ẹld), made like something else
moist, slightly wet
mon ster (mon′stėr), a huge creature with a strange shape
mor sel (môr′sl), a little bit; a mouthful
mo tion less (mō′shọn-les), not moving
mounted, got up on the animal's back
mourn ing (mōr′ning), showing or feeling sorrow for the death of someone
murmur, low sound or noise

N

Na nou (na-nö′)
nas tur tium (nạs-tėr′shium), a showy plant with red or yellow flowers

---

at, cāme, fär, âll, ȧsk, cãre, ạlone; end, bē, hėr, towẹl; it, līne; on, mōre, tö, ôff, actọr; oil, out; up, ūse, pụt, natūre; picţure; th, thin; ŦH, then. See full key on p. 375.

BASIC READERS—BOOK FOUR

natives (nā′tivz), people born in a certain place or country
nimble (nim′bl), quick-moving
noble warrior (nō′bl wor′i-ėr), one who does great deeds in war
notch, a cut like the letter V
Nouvilo (nö-vē′lō)

P

Pana kilele (pän′a̧ ki-lä′lē)
panted, spoke with short, quick breaths
particular (pär-tik′ū-lar̞), hard to please; a certain one
partridge (pär′trij)
pass, mountain pass (pȧs), a road through the mountains, hard to travel over
pasture (pȧs′tūr), a grassy field or hillside where horses and cattle can feed
Patrasche (pa̧-träsh′)
paused (pâzd), stopped for a time
peaks, the pointed tops of hills or mountains
peal, a loud sound, as of bells or laughter
pelting, striking or beating with something thrown
pewter (pū′tėr), a silver-like metal often used for plates, spoons, etc.
Philemon (fi-lē′mo̧n)
physical director (fiz′i-ka̧l di-rek′-tor̞), the man in charge of plays and games at a school
pinnacles (pin′a̧-klz), the highest points on buildings or mountains
pioneer (pī-o̧-nēr′), a person who is among the first to make a home in a new place
piteously (pit′ȩ̄-us-li), in a begging way
pleaded, begged
plentiful, large; full; having as much as is needed

plunged (plunjd), leaped or rushed into
porridge (por′ij), food made by boiling corn-meal in water or milk
porter (pōr′tėr), one who carries loads or baggage for pay
potter, a person who makes dishes, jars, and pots from clay
pottery, bowls, jugs, jars, etc., made from clay or stone
prairie (prãr′i), a wide, grassy piece of land with no trees
presently (prez′ȩnt-li), after a little while; by and by
prim, very neat and nice
procession (prō-sesh′o̧n), line of people or objects moving along in order
provide (prō-vīd′), give; make ready for; prepare
public, for everybody
purpose, all to no purpose (pėr′po̧s), without finding them

Q

Quaker (kwā′kėr), one of a religious group who call themselves Friends
quills (kwilz), sharp, stiff spikes on a porcupine; large, stiff feathers

R

raging (rā′jing), very stormy or angry
raven (rā′vn), a black bird, larger than the crow
rebels (reb′ȩlz), people who are fighting against those who rule over them, because they wish to rule themselves
Regin (rē′gin)
relish (rel′ish), enjoy
remain, stay
remarked (rȩ̄-märkt′), said

GLOSSARY 381

Rev o lu tion a ry War (rev-ō-lū′shǫn-ā-ri), war fought against England by the Americans to win their freedom
rick sha (rik′shä), small two-wheeled cart pulled by one or two men. See picture on page 152.
ripple, form small waves
roamed, wandered
Ro land (rō′lạnd)
rub down (rub′doun), rubbing
Rum ple stilt skin (rum-pl-stilt′skin)
rus tling (rus′ling), a sound like that made by shaking leaves or straw

S

sa fa ri (są-fä′rē), a journey or march
sampler, a piece of fine needlework made to show how well the worker can sew
Sar a cens (sar′ą-sęnz)
sas sa fras (sas′ą-fras), the bark from the root of the sassafras tree, used as a medicine and for flavoring candy and other foods
scanty, small
scarce ly (skârs′li), hardly
scar let (skär′let), bright red in color
scent (sent), smell; odor
scep ter (sep′tėr), a staff carried by a king to show that he has the right to rule
school of fish, a large number of fish swimming together
scowl ing (skou′ling), frowning
sheep-shearers, men who clip the wool from sheep
shelter, a covering; a safe place
shirk, try to get out of work
shuddering, trembling or shaking with fear
Si gurd (sē′gėrd)
six pence (siks′pęns), an English piece of money, worth about twelve cents of American money
sketched (skecht), drew a hasty picture of
slabs, thick pieces
slay, kill
slope, side of hill or mountain
slug gards (slug′ạrdz), lazy persons
smith, a person who makes things of iron or other metal
smith y (smiᴛʜ′i or smith′i), the workshop of a smith
snap drag on (snap′drag′ǫn), a bright-colored garden flower
snorted, forced the breath violently through the nose with a loud sound
snug gled (snug′ld), lay close to; nestled
sorted, separated according to size or kind
spear, long, sharp-pointed pole used in fighting
spe cial-delivery stamp (spesh′ạl), a kind of stamp put on letters or packages so that they will be delivered sooner than other mail
sped, hurried
spellbound, too surprised and interested to move
spick and span, fresh and clean
spires, steeples
spryest, quickest; most active
Squan to (skwän′tō)
staggered, stumbled
steed, a fine, lively riding horse
stern, hard; severe; the back part of a boat

---

at, cāme, fär, âll, ȧsk, cāre, ạlone; end, bē, hėr, towęl; it, līne; on, mōre, tö, ôff, actǫr; oil, out; up, ūse, pṳt, natųre; picture; th, thin; ᴛʜ, then. See full key on p. 375

streaming, flying straight out, as a flag
struggled (strug′ld), worked hard; fought hard against enemies
sturdy, strong
sure of foot, does not stumble or fall while walking or climbing
surface (sėr′fās), the top or outside of anything
swarmed (swârmd), came out in crowds, as ants or bees
swift-footed, able to run very fast
swing, in full swing, going on very busily
Swiss (swis), belonging to the country or people of Switzerland
swoop (swöp), fly down swiftly

T

tallow (tal′ō), hard fat from cows or sheep
tend, take care of
thicket, trees and bushes growing close together
thoughtfully (thôt′fŭl-i), thinking hard; being careful
throb, beat, as the heart beats
thronging, crowded
thus, so
thyme (tīm), a wild, sweet-smelling plant
Tintourlet (tan-tör-lā′)
tiny (tī′ni), very small
Tonino (tō-nē′nō)
town meeting, meeting of all the men living in the town to carry on the business of the town
tread (tred), stamp or press out with the feet
treasure (trezh′ụr), money, jewels, and the like
trillium (tril′i-um), a plant with three leaves around a single flower
trim, neat and in good order
tugged (tugd), pulled hard
turret (tur′et), a small tower
twigs, the smallest branches on a tree or bush
twilight (twī′līt), the time just before dark
twining (twī′ning), winding
twirling, whirling

U

umpire (um′pir), one who sees that a game is played fairly
uncommon (un-kom′ọn), not common; not well-known; strange

V

vacant (vā′kạnt), not used; empty
Vence (väns)
vow (vou), a solemn promise

W

wail, a long cry of pain
wandered (won′dėrd), went off or away
warming pan, a covered pan for holding live coals of fire. In the early days of our country, such a pan was used to warm beds.
warning (wâr′ning), giving notice of danger
warriors (wor′i-ėrz), fighting men
"Wazungu" (wä-zöng′gü)
weapons (wep′ọnz), things used to fight with
weary (wēr′i), tired; worn-out
weld, join together by melting and hammering

GLOSSARY

wharves (hwârvz), places for boats to land
whisk, move or carry something away quickly
winding (wīn′ding), twisting or turning
witty (wit′i), amusing; funny
wizard (wiz′ȧrd), one able to do magic tricks
woe betide it, trouble will come of it

wonder-working, doing strange and wonderful things
wore on, passed slowly away
wry (rī), unpleasant, as if he did not like to think about it

Y

yonder (yon′dėr), over there
Yule log, large log burned at Christmas time

---

at, cāme, fär, âll, ȧsk, cāre, ạlone; end, bē, her, towẹl; it, līne; on, mōre, tö, ôff, actọr; oil, out; up, ūse, put, natụre; picṭure; th, thin; ₮H, then. See full key on p. 375.